Life

P9-BIP-891

elevate science

SAVVAS
LEARNING COMPANY

AUTHORS

You're an author!

As you write in this science book, your answers and personal discoveries will be recorded for you to keep, making this book unique to you. That is why you are one of the primary authors of this book.

🖊 **In the space below, print your name, school, town, and state. Then write a short autobiography that includes your interests and accomplishments.**

YOUR NAME ....

SCHOOL ....

TOWN, STATE ....

AUTOBIOGRAPHY ....

Your Photo

ISBN-13: 978-1-418-31052-3
ISBN-10:   1-418-31052-2

6   23

Program Authors

ZIPPORAH MILLER, Ed.D.

Coordinator for K-12 Science Programs, Anne Arundel County Public Schools

Dr. Zipporah Miller currently serves as the Senior Manager for Organizational Learning with the Anne Arundel County Public School System. Prior to that she served as the K-12 Coordinator for science in Anne Arundel County. She conducts national training to science stakeholders on the Next Generation Science Standards. Dr. Miller also served as the Associate Executive Director for Professional Development Programs and conferences at the National Science Teachers Association (NSTA) and served as a reviewer during the development of Next Generation Science Standards. Dr. Miller holds a doctoral degree from the University of Maryland College Park, a master's degree in school administration and supervision from Bowie State University and a bachelor's degree from Chadron State College.

MICHAEL J. PADILLA, Ph.D.

Professor Emeritus, Eugene P. Moore School of Education, Clemson University, Clemson, South Carolina

Michael J. Padilla taught science in middle and secondary schools, has more than 30 years of experience educating middle-school science teachers, and served as one of the writers of the 1996 U.S. National Science Education Standards. In recent years Mike has focused on teaching science to English Language Learners. His extensive experience as Principal Investigator on numerous National Science Foundation and U.S. Department of Education grants resulted in more than $35 million in funding to improve science education. He served as president of the National Science Teachers Association, the world's largest science teaching organization, in 2005–6.

MICHAEL E. WYSESSION, Ph.D

Professor of Earth and Planetary Sciences, Washington University, St. Louis, Missouri

Author of more than 100 science and science education publications, Dr. Wysession was awarded the prestigious National Science Foundation Presidential Faculty Fellowship and Packard Foundation Fellowship for his research in geophysics, primarily focused on using seismic tomography to determine the forces driving plate tectonics. Dr. Wysession is also a leader in geoscience literacy and education; he is the chair of the Earth Science Literacy Initiative, the author of several popular video lectures on geology in the *Great Courses* series, and a lead writer of the *Next Generation Science Standards**.

*Next Generation Science Standards is a registered trademark of WestEd. Neither WestEd nor the lead states and partners that developed the Next Generation Science Standards were involved in the production of this product, and do not endorse it. NGSS Lead States. 2013. *Next Generation Science Standards: For States, By States.* Washington, DC: The National Academies Press.

REVIEWERS

Program Consultants

Carol Baker
Science Curriculum

Dr. Carol K. Baker is superintendent for Lyons Elementary K-8 School District in Lyons, Illinois. Prior to this, she was Director of Curriculum for Science and Music in Oak Lawn, Illinois. Before this she taught Physics and Earth Science for 18 years. In the recent past, Dr. Baker also wrote assessment questions for ACT (EXPLORE and PLAN), was elected president of the Illinois Science Teachers Association from 2011–2013, and served as a member of the Museum of Science and Industry (Chicago) advisory board. She is a writer of the Next Generation Science Standards. Dr. Baker received her B.S. in Physics and a science teaching certification. She completed her master's of Educational Administration (K-12) and earned her doctorate in Educational Leadership.

Jim Cummins
ELL

Dr. Cummins's research focuses on literacy development in multilingual schools and the role technology plays in learning across the curriculum. *Elevate Science* incorporates research-based principles for integrating language with the teaching of academic content based on Dr. Cummins's work.

Elfrieda Hiebert
Literacy

Dr. Hiebert, a former primary-school teacher, is President and CEO of TextProject, a non-profit aimed at providing open-access resources for instruction of beginning and struggling readers, She is also a research associate at the University of California Santa Cruz. Her research addresses how fluency, vocabulary, and knowledge can be fostered through appropriate texts, and her contributions have been recognized through awards such as the Oscar Causey Award for Outstanding Contributions to Reading Research (Literacy Research Association, 2015), Research to Practice award (American Educational Research Association, 2013), and the William S. Gray Citation of Merit Award for Outstanding Contributions to Reading Research (International Reading Association, 2008).

Content Reviewers

Alex Blom, Ph.D.
Associate Professor
Department Of Physical Sciences
Alverno College
Milwaukee, Wisconsin

Joy Branlund, Ph.D.
Department of Physical Science
Southwestern Illinois College
Granite City, Illinois

Judy Calhoun
Associate Professor
Physical Sciences
Alverno College
Milwaukee, Wisconsin

Stefan Debbert
Associate Professor of Chemistry
Lawrence University
Appleton, Wisconsin

Diane Doser
Professor
Department of Geological Sciences
University of Texas at El Paso
El Paso, Texas

Rick Duhrkopf, Ph.D.
Department of Biology
Baylor University
Waco, Texas

Jennifer Liang
University of Minnesota Duluth
Duluth, Minnesota

Heather Mernitz, Ph.D.
Associate Professor of Physical Sciences
Alverno College
Milwaukee, Wisconsin

Joseph McCullough, Ph.D.
Cabrillo College
Aptos, California

Katie M. Nemeth, Ph.D.
Assistant Professor
College of Science and Engineering
University of Minnesota Duluth
Duluth, Minnesota

Maik Pertermann
Department of Geology
Western Wyoming Community College
Rock Springs, Wyoming

Scott Rochette
Department of the Earth Sciences
The College at Brockport
 State University of New York
Brockport, New York

David Schuster
Washington University in St Louis
St. Louis, Missouri

Shannon Stevenson
Department of Biology
University of Minnesota Duluth
Duluth, Minnesota

Paul Stoddard, Ph.D.
Department of Geology and
 Environmental Geosciences
Northern Illinois University
DeKalb, Illinois

Nancy Taylor
American Public University
Charles Town, West Virginia

Teacher Reviewers

Rita Armstrong
Los Cerritos Middle School
Thousand Oaks, California

Tyler C. Britt, Ed.S.
Curriculum & Instructional
Practice Coordinator
Raytown Quality Schools
Raytown, Missouri

Holly Bowser
Barstow High School
Barstow, California

David Budai
Coachella Valley Unified School District
Coachella, California

A. Colleen Campos
Grandview High School
Aurora, Colorado

Jodi DeRoos
Mojave River Academy
Colton, California

Colleen Duncan
Moore Middle School
Redlands, California

Nicole Hawke
Westside Elementary
Thermal, California

Margaret Henry
Lebanon Junior High School
Lebanon, Ohio

Ashley Humphrey
Riverside Preparatory Elementary
Oro Grande, California

Adrianne Kilzer
Riverside Preparatory Elementary
Oro Grande, California

Danielle King
Barstow Unified School District
Barstow, California

Kathryn Kooyman
Riverside Preparatory Elementary
Oro Grande, California

Esther Leonard M.Ed. and L.M.T.
Gifted and Talented Implementation Specialist
San Antonio Independent School District
San Antonio, Texas

Diana M. Maiorca, M.Ed.
Los Cerritos Middle School
Thousand Oaks, California

Kevin J. Maser, Ed.D.
H. Frank Carey Jr/Sr High School
Franklin Square, New York

Corey Mayle
Brogden Middle School
Durham, North Carolina

Keith McCarthy
George Washington Middle School
Wayne, New Jersey

Rudolph Patterson
Cobalt Institute of Math and Science
Victorville, California

Yolanda O. Peña
John F. Kennedy Junior High School
West Valley City, Utah

Stacey Phelps
Mojave River Academy
Oro Grande, California

Susan Pierce
Bryn Mawr Elementary
Redlands Unified School District
Redlands, California

Cristina Ramos
Mentone Elementary School
Redlands Unified School District
Mentone, California

Mary Regis
Franklin Elementary School
Redlands, California

Bryna Selig
Gaithersburg Middle School
Gaithersburg, Maryland

Pat (Patricia) Shane, Ph.D.
STEM & ELA Education Consultant
Chapel Hill, North Carolina

Elena Valencia
Coral Mountain Academy
Coachella, California

Janelle Vecchio
Mission Elementary School
Redlands, California

Brittney Wells
Riverside Preparatory Elementary
Oro Grande, California

Kristina Williams
Sequoia Middle School
Newbury Park, California

Safety Reviewers

Douglas Mandt, M.S.
Science Education Consultant
Edgewood, Washington

Juliana Textley, Ph.D.
Author, NSTA books on school science safety
Adjunct Professor
Lesley University
Cambridge, Massachusetts

California Spotlight
Instructional Segment 3

When Salmon Don't Run

TOPIC 7 Reproduction and Growth 8

Investigative Phenomenon How can you use evidence to explain what factors influence the growth of organisms and their ability to reproduce?

Quest PBL Construction Without Destruction 10

🕐 MS-LS1-4, MS-LS1-5, MS-LS3-2, EP&CIIc, EP&CIVb

HANDS-ON LABS

*u*Connect
*u*Investigate
*u*Demonstrate

HANDS-ON LABS

*u*Connect
*u*Investigate
*u*Demonstrate

Elevate your thinking!

California Elevate Science takes science to a whole new level and lets you take ownership of your learning. Explore science in the world around you. Investigate how things work. Think critically and solve problems! *California Elevate Science* helps you think like a scientist, so you're ready for a world of discoveries.

Exploring California

California spotlights explore California phenomena. Topic Quests help connect lesson concepts together and reflect 3-dimensional learning.

- Science concepts organized around phenomena
- Topics weave together 3-D learning
- Engineering focused on solving problems and improving designs

Student Discourse

California Elevate Science promotes active discussion, higher order thinking and analysis and prepares you for high school through:

- High-level write-in prompts
- Evidence-based arguments
- Practice in speaking and writing

California Spotlight
Instructional Segment 2

Before the Topics
Identify the Problem

California Flood Management

Phenomenon In February of 2017, workers at the Orov...

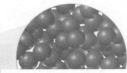 **Quest** KICKOFF

How can you use solids, liquids, and gases to lift a car?

STEM Phenomenon Auto mechanics often need to go under cars to repair the parts in the under-carriage, such as the shocks and exhaust...

Model It

Crystalline and Amorphous Solids
Figure 5 ✏ A pat of butter is an amorphous solid. The particles that make up the butter are not arranged in a regular pattern. The sapphire gem stones are crystalline solids. Draw what you think the particles look like in a crystalline solid.

☑ **READING CHECK** Explain
In your own words, explain the main differences between crystalline solids and amorphous solids.

Quest CHECK-IN

In this lesson, you learned what happens to the particles of substances during melting, freezing, evaporation, boiling, condensation, and sublimation. You also thought about how thermal energy plays a role in these changes of state.

Predict Why do you need to take the temperature of the surroundings into consideration when designing a system with materials that can change state?

Academic Vocabulary

In orange juice, bits of pulp are suspended in liquid. Explain what you think *suspended* means.

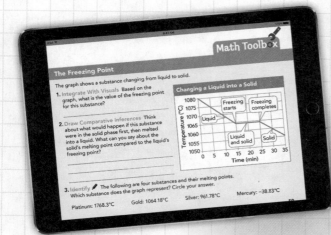

Build Literacy Skills

By connecting science to other disciplines like:

- Mathematics
- Reading and Writing
- STEM/Engineering

Focus on Inquiry

Case studies put you in the shoes of a scientist to solve real-world mysteries using real data. You will be able to:

- Analyze data
- Formulate claims
- Build evidence-based arguments

Case Study

MS-PS1-4

RiSiNG to the OCCASiON: Charles's Law in the Oven!

Have you ever baked bread or rolls? If so, you probably observed that during baking, the bread rises, increasing in volume. What causes this to happen? The answer lies in chemistry.

Chemistry in Baking

Chemistry and baking go together naturally. In fact, chemistry affects every aspect of preparing food.

In the heat of an oven, gas bubbles in bread

Enter the Digital Classroom

Virtual labs, 3-D expeditions, and dynamic videos take science beyond the classroom.

- Open-ended virtual labs
- Google Expeditions and field trips
- NBC Learn videos

After watching the Quest Kickoff video about how coastal engineers study and reduce coastal erosion, complete the 3-2-1 activity.

How do human activities affect the growth and reproduction of living organisms?

Explore It

Look at the picture. What do you observe? What questions do you have about the phenomenon? Write your observations and questions in the space below.

....
....
....
....
....
....
....
....
....
....
....
....
....
....
....
....
....
....
....
....

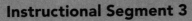
MS-LS1-4, MS-LS1-5, MS-LS3-1,
MS-LS3-2, MS-LS4-4, MS-LS4-5,
MS-ETS1-1, EP&CIIc, EP&CIVb

Inquiry

- How do cells know what to do and how to accomplish it?
- Why do children look like their parents?
- What causes differences between individuals?

Topics

7 Reproduction and Growth
8 Genes and Heredity

Before the Topic

Identify the Problem

When Salmon Don't Run

Phenomenon Chinook salmon and steelhead trout once flourished in California. For several millennia, these native fish species lived in rivers that were very different from the ones that flow through California today. Human activities have altered fish habitats, and low genetic diversity is to blame for their decline in number. Climate change, for instance, has affected the health of many river ecosystems.

Some native trout and salmon populations are on the decline in California.

Every year, salmon from the ocean travel up river to their birthplace to spawn, or lay eggs, in freshwater. This yearly mass movement of fish up river is called a run.

Many game fishers practice catch-and-release with steelhead trout to help increase their probability of surviving and reproducing.

Changing Conditions and Permanent Change

California is home to a great diversity of salmon and trout species. To support the diversity of species and increase their chance of survival, fish need a place to spawn. The snow melt that runs off mountain ranges like the Sierra Nevadas provides fresh cold water for rivers and streams needed for spawning. But those conditions are changing, and many of California's fish are affected. Dams, which humans construct to control the flow of water, destroyed their habitat. Dams stop the run and isolate fish from one another downstream as water disappears. This isolation decreases genetic diversity. They also could not compete with the non-native fish that were introduced into the river system.

Due to the rising temperatures associated with climate change, river water is getting warmer. For some native fish species, low genetic diversity makes this change intolerable. They do not inherit traits that favor a change in temperature. Complete the graph to compare the impact of climate change on native and non-native fish species.

The common carp is a non-native species. It now outnumbers native California species, such as the steelhead trout and salmon.

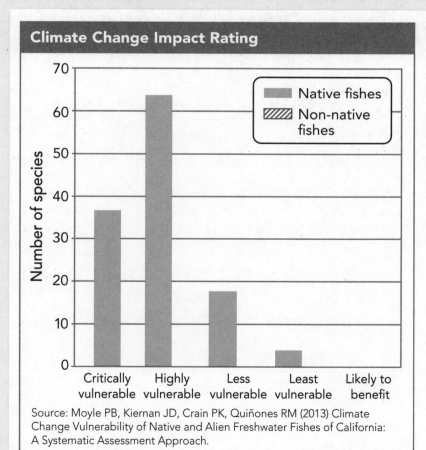

Climate Change Impact Rating

Number of species (y-axis: 0, 10, 20, 30, 40, 50, 60, 70)

Legend:
- Native fishes
- Non-native fishes

x-axis categories: Critically vulnerable, Highly vulnerable, Less vulnerable, Least vulnerable, Likely to benefit

Source: Moyle PB, Kiernan JD, Crain PK, Quiñones RM (2013) Climate Change Vulnerability of Native and Alien Freshwater Fishes of California: A Systematic Assessment Approach.

If a species is vulnerable, that means hotter temperatures can harm it.

1. **SEP Use Mathematics** 🖊 About 8 non-native species are highly vulnerable to climate change, 14 are less vulnerable, 16 are least vulnerable, and 6 are likely to benefit. Use the data to complete the histogram.

2. **SEP Interpret Data** How does the data for native fishes compare to the data for non-native fishes?

....
....
....
....
....

Changing Landscapes and Habitat Loss

Human activities, including burning fossil fuels and others that have contributed to global warming, have seriously impacted rivers and harmed many native fish species. When people divert water for farm use, they change the natural course of that water and isolate the fish. When people build dams, they change habitats both up and downstream. When gravel is mined out of riverbeds, humans are removing safe areas for fish to lay their eggs.

Six thousand miles of rivers and creeks flowing through California's Central Valley once provided safe fish habitats. Every spring, 600,000 Chinook salmon could run upstream to the place they were born. There, they would start the cycle of life all over again. But that changed when humans started building dams. By 1997, the number of Chinook salmon dropped below 6,000. Today, the spring-run Chinook salmon inhabit less than 300 river miles, mostly in the Sacramento River. And there are no more spring-run Chinook in the San Joaquin River. Look at the map to see the historic range of spring-run Chinook salmon.

In the Central Valley, the spring run for Chinook salmon takes place in the Antelope, Beegum, Butte, Deer, and Mill Creeks. These five creeks feed the Sacramento River.

SEP Analyze Data ✏️
Highlight the creeks on the map and then draw a circle around them.

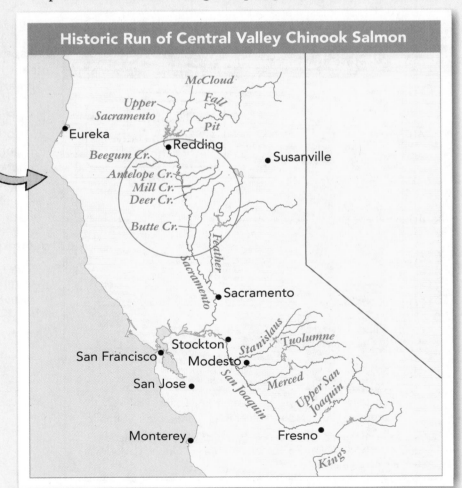

Historic Run of Central Valley Chinook Salmon

One River, Many Habitats

Salmon and steelhead trout are anadromous (UH-nad-ru-mus) fish. Because of their genetic make-up, they spend most of their lives in salty ocean water but reproduce in fresh water. Rivers offer safe places for each phase of life, beginning with reproduction. Young salmon eat insects. Streams flowing through areas with overhanging tree branches and grasses provide plenty of food. River beds with old logs and branches offer shelter. When Chinook move back to the ocean, they stop at marshes. These natural borders between freshwater and salt water give their bodies a chance to get used to being in salt water.

The Sacramento and San Joaquin rivers share a delta. The estuary, or area of water where a river meets the ocean, provides places where young fish can develop.

Salmon River in western Siskiyou County, California

Salmon and steelhead both need specific and various sizes of gravels to lay their eggs.

A New Lease on Life

In this segment you will learn about the reproduction and growth of plants and animals. You will investigate how animal behaviors increase their chances of reproducing. You will learn about how traits are inherited. You will also learn about the importance of genetic diversity and how differences can help, hurt, or not affect a population. You will also explore different genetic technologies. Scientists and wildlife managers study reproduction and inheritance so they can figure out the best ways to save a species.

Humans can help salmon, trout, and other native freshwater fish survive the impacts of global warming. People can also help undo some of the harm they have already caused. Many environmental groups specialize in fish conservation. Some rescue fish stranded in streams when water is running too low. Others work to restore native habitats. Some groups are advocates. For example, during the drought in 2014, the Hoopa Valley Tribe in northwestern California urged the federal government to release water from the Trinity River dam in Weatherville. They took action to protect the fish downstream.

These Department of Fish and Game workers are in the process of relocating trout from Caples Lake near Kirkwood, California.

SEP Construct Explanations What impact does relocating fish species have on the population Explain.

....

....

What questions can you ask to help you make sense of this phenomena?

Reproduction and Growth

Investigative Phenomenon
How can you use evidence to explain what factors influence the growth of organisms and their ability to reproduce?

Can desert animals be affected by drought?

MS-LS1-4 Use argument based on empirical evidence and scientific reasoning to support an explanation for how characteristic animal behaviors and specialized plant structures affect the probability of successful reproduction of animals and plants respectively.

MS-LS1-5 Construct a scientific explanation based on evidence for how environmental and genetic factors influence the growth of organisms.

MS-LS3-2 Develop and use a model to describe why asexual reproduction results in offspring with identical genetic information and sexual reproduction results in offspring with genetic variation.

EP&CIIc Students should be developing an understanding that the expansion and operation of human communities influences the geographic extent, composition, biological diversity, and viability of natural systems.

EP&CIVb Students should be developing an understanding that the byproducts of human activity are not readily prevented from entering natural systems and may be beneficial, neutral, or detrimental in their effect.

и**Connect** Use a model to investigate how parental care can influence the survival of offspring.

What questions do you have about the phenomenon?

....
....
....
....
....
....
....
....
....
....

Quest PBL

How can we reduce the impact of construction on plants and animals?

Figure It Out Environmental scientists study habitats and the organisms that live there. They investigate how the availability of resources—such as water, food, and space—affects the ability of plants and animals to survive and reproduce. In this Quest activity, you will consider how to build a basketball court on school grounds, with minimal impact on local plants and animals. In digital activities, you will explore the factors that affect plant and animal growth and reproduction. By applying what you have learned, you will develop a construction proposal for the basketball court.

 INTERACTIVITY

Construction Without Destruction

 MS-LS1-5, EP&CIIc

NBC LEARN ▶ VIDEO

After watching the video, which explores how construction impacts habitats and organisms, consider the issue on a local level. Choose a plant or animal, and then explain how human activity in your town or city affects the organism.

....
....
....
....
....
....
....
....
....

IN LESSON 1
How do different organisms reproduce? Think about how the court's impact on the habitat might affect the ability of organisms to survive and reproduce there.

IN LESSON 2
How do living things inherit traits from their parents? Consider how changes to an organism's environment due to construction might disrupt this process.

Quest CHECK-IN

IN LESSON 3
What effect might tree removal and construction work have on plants in the area? Assess the environmental impact on the ability of the plants to survive and reproduce.

 INTERACTIVITY

Protect the Plants

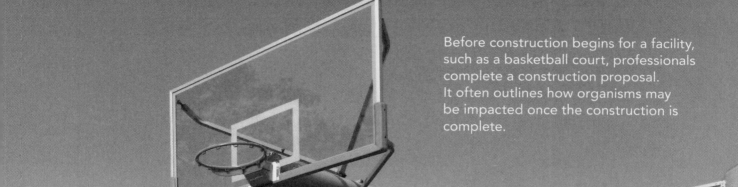

Before construction begins for a facility, such as a basketball court, professionals complete a construction proposal. It often outlines how organisms may be impacted once the construction is complete.

Quest CHECK-IN

IN LESSON 4

How does construction work impact animals? Think about how construction noise might interfere with the ability of an organism to reproduce successfully.

👆 INTERACTIVITY

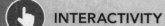
The Mating Game

Quest CHECK-IN

IN LESSON 5

STEM How can the impact of the court's location and construction be minimized? Develop a plan that ensures the successful survival and reproduction of plants and animals.

👆 INTERACTIVITY

Make Your Construction Case

Quest FINDINGS

Complete the Quest!

Present your construction plan using the information and data that you have collected as evidence to support your recommendations.

👆 INTERACTIVITY

Reflect on Your Basketball Court Plans

11

HANDS-ON LAB

uInvestigate Develop and use models of asexual and sexual reproduction to compare how genetic information is passed from parent(s) to offspring.

MS-LS3-2 Develop and use a model to describe why asexual reproduction results in offspring with identical genetic information and sexual reproduction results in offspring with genetic variation.

Connect It !

✎ **The pictures show offspring with their mothers. Circle the offspring you think might look like the father.**

SEP Construct Explanations Summarize what you already know about how the three kinds of animals in the picture produce offspring.

....

....

....

....

....

....

Asexual and Sexual Reproduction

Living things reproduce. Giraffes make more giraffes, hermit crabs make more hermit crabs, and bald eagles make more bald eagles. Some animals produce offspring that look exactly like the parent. Others, such as humans and the animals in **Figure 1,** produce offspring that look different from the parents.

Animals use one of two main methods—asexual or sexual reproduction—to produce offspring. Reproduction guarantees that a species' genes are passed on to the next generation.

Asexual Reproduction A reproductive process that involves only one parent and produces offspring that are genetically identical to the parent is called **asexual reproduction**. It is the simplest form of reproduction. Animals such as sponges, corals, and certain jellyfish reproduce asexually.

One form of asexual reproduction is **fragmentation**. During fragmentation, a new organism forms from a piece of the original. For example, one feather duster worm can start a new colony (**Figure 2**). Another method of asexual reproduction is called budding. In this process, a new animal grows out from the parent until it fully matures and breaks off. Sponges and some sea anemones reproduce in this way.

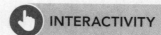

INTERACTIVITY

Consider the traits that make you unique.

Reflect What do you think is the benefit of reproducing asexually? In your science notebook, explain how asexual reproduction could give some animals an advantage.

Academic Vocabulary

The root of fragmentation is fragment. How does this relate to its meaning?

....

....

....

....

....

Reproduction Results in Offspring
Figure 1 All living things have the ability to reproduce.

Sexual Reproduction Consider the variety of trees, birds, fish, and plants in the world around you. Clearly, many life forms are unique. When organisms reproduce sexually, their offspring display a variety of traits. Even members of the same family are not exact copies of each other. Sexual reproduction is responsible for the variety of life you see.

In **sexual reproduction**, two parents combine their genetic material to produce a new organism that differs from both parents. Sexual reproduction involves an egg cell and a sperm cell joining to form a new cell in a process called **fertilization**. Sperm cells are from the father and contribute the father's half of the chromosomes, or structures that contain genetic information. Egg cells are from the mother and contribute the mother's half of the chromosomes. When fertilization occurs, a full set of chromosomes is present in the new cell.

Because offspring receive roughly half their genetic information from each parent, they receive a combination of specific characteristics. A specific characteristic that an organism can pass to its offspring through its genes is called a **trait**. A **gene** is a sequence of DNA that determines a trait and is passed from parent to offspring. As a result, offspring may look very similar to their parents, or they may look very different, like the California dairy cows in **Figure 2**. These differences are known as variations, and they are what make you different from your siblings. Individual variations depend on which genes were passed on from each parent.

Sexual vs. Asexual Reproduction

Figure 2 (top) One feather duster worm can start a new colony. (bottom) A California dairy calf and her mother.

1. **Claim** 🖋 Circle the image of sexually reproducing organisms.

2. **Evidence** What evidence did you use to support your claim?

....

....

3. **Reasoning** Explain how your evidence supports your claim.

....

....

....

....

....

....

Model It!

SEP Develop Models 🖋 Suppose a feather duster worm produces offspring through asexual reproduction and two neighborhood dogs produce offspring through sexual reproduction. Draw a picture that shows how genetic information is passed down in each method of reproduction. Label the traits passed on to each offspring from the parent(s). Use your model to explain to a partner how genetic information is passed down in both types of reproduction.

Comparing Types of Reproduction

Both methods of reproduction have advantages and disadvantages. Organisms that reproduce asexually do not have to find a mate. They can also produce many offspring fairly quickly. The downside is that all of the offspring have exactly the same genetic makeup as the parent. This can be a problem if the environment changes. If one individual organism is unable to survive the change, then chances are the rest of the identical offspring will not be able to survive it either.

Organisms that reproduce sexually pass on chromosomes with genetic variation. This variation may increase the chances their offspring could survive a changing environment. It is possible that they received a gene from a parent that would help them adapt to the changing environment. One potential downside of sexual reproduction is that the organism needs to find a mate. This can sometimes be a problem for animals, such as polar bears, that live in remote areas.

☑ CHECK POINT **Cite Textual Evidence** What are some advantages of organisms reproducing sexually?

....

....

....

👆 **INTERACTIVITY**

Explore the similarities and differences between sexual and asexual reproduction.

HANDS-ON LAB

ⁿ**Investigate** Develop and use models of asexual and sexual reproduction to compare how genetic information is passed from parent(s) to offspring.

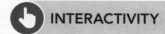

Math Toolbox

Sexual Reproduction

Gestation is the time period between fertilization and birth. The data in the table are based on recorded observations from hundreds of pregnant individuals in each species.

Animal	Gestation Range (days)	Median Gestation Time (days)	Bottom Quartile Median (days)	Top Quartile Median (days)
Hamster	16–23	20	17	22
Red Fox	49–55	52	50	53
Gerbil	22–26	24	23	25
Leopard	91–95	93	92	94

1. **Distinguish Relationships** What is the relationship between the size of the animal and how long it takes for its offspring to develop?

....

....

2. **Summarize Distributions** 🖊 Choose two species from the table and construct a box plot for each one.

15

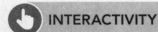
Inherited Traits

When sperm and egg cells come together, genetic information from the mother and father mix. **Inheritance** is the process by which an offspring receives genes from its parents. Genes are located on chromosomes and determine the factors that control a trait. Each trait is determined by a pair of genes, with one gene from the mother and one from the father. Sometimes the pair of genes are the same. At other times, there are two different genes in the pair.

For example, imagine a mouse with white fur and a mouse with brown fur have offspring. The genes for fur color from each parent are different. As shown in **Figure 3,** some of the offspring produced may be brown, some may be white, and others may be combinations of more than one color. Each offspring's fur color depends on how its inherited genes combine.

An **allele** is a different form of the same gene. One allele is received from each parent, and the combination of alleles determines which traits the offspring will have. In the simplest case, alleles are either dominant or recessive. If an offspring inherits a dominant allele from either parent, that trait will always show up in the offspring. But, if the offspring inherits recessive alleles from each parent, a recessive trait will show. This relationship allows parents with two dominant alleles to pass on recessive alleles to their offspring. For example, two brown-eyed people may have a blue-eyed child. However, most genetic traits do not follow these simple patterns of dominant and recessive inheritance.

☑ LESSON 1 Check

1. **Distinguish Relationships** What does inheritance mean in terms of reproduction?

....

....

....

....

....

2. **Explain Phenomena** What happens if an offspring inherits a dominant allele from one of its parents?

....

....

....

....

....

3. **CCC Patterns** Explain why sexual reproduction results in offspring with more genetic variation than asexual reproduction.

....

....

....

....

....

....

....

....

....

....

....

4. **SEP Use Models** 🖊 In the space below, draw a Venn diagram comparing and contrasting asexual reproduction and sexual reproduction.

② Patterns of Inheritance

HANDS-ON LAB

ᵤInvestigate Explore cross-pollination by examining the parts of a flower.

MS-LS3-2 Develop and use a model to describe why asexual reproduction results in offspring with identical genetic information and sexual reproduction results in offspring with genetic variation.

Connect It !

🖊 **Male house finches express the trait for red feather color. Circle the male house finch in the photo.**

Predict 🖊 List four more visible characteristics that these birds will pass on to their offspring. Then list the inherited trait that their offspring will possess.

Visible Characteristics	Inherited Traits
grayish bill color	bill color

Apply Concepts Will their offspring look exactly like the parents? Explain.

....

....

Mendel's Observations

Like all other organisms, the finches in **Figure 1** pass their traits to their offspring. To better understand **heredity**, the passing of traits from parents to offspring, it is important to learn about the history behind the science. In the 1800s, a European monk named Gregor Mendel studied heredity. Mendel's job at the monastery was to tend the garden. After several years of growing pea plants, he became very familiar with the traits pea plants could have. Some plants grew tall, while others were short. Some produced green seeds, while others produced yellow.

Mendel's Experiments Mendel's studies became some of the most important in biology because he was one of the first to **quantify** his results. He collected, recorded, and analyzed data from the thousands of tests that he ran.

The experiments Mendel performed involved **pollination**, the transfer of the male flower part of a pea plant to the female flower part, to get a desired trait. Mendel wanted to see what would happen with pea plants when he crossed different traits: short and tall, yellow seeds and green seeds, and so on. Because of his detailed work with heredity, Mendel is often referred to as the "father of modern genetics."

HANDS-ON LAB

Explore how human height is inherited.

Academic Vocabulary

In Latin, *quantus* means "how much." Have you heard the word quantify used before? Does it remind you of any other words?

....

....

....

....

Passing on Traits

Figure 1 House finches are common yard and feeder birds in California. Male and female house finches share many traits, but also have several that make them unique.

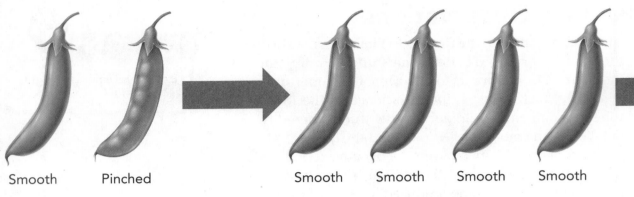

Smooth   Pinched   Smooth   Smooth   Smooth   Smooth

P generation   **F₁ generation**

Pea Pod Shape

Figure 2 ✏ Circle the pod shape in the P generation that has the dominant trait.

Parents and Offspring

When Mendel cross-pollinated, or crossed, a tall plant with a short one, all of the offspring were tall. The tall plant and short plant that were crossed are called the parent plants, or P generation. The offspring are called the F_1, or first filial generation. The term *filial* originates from the Latin terms *filius* and *filia*, which mean "son" and "daughter," respectively.

Mendel examined several traits of pea plants. Through his experimentation, he discovered that certain patterns formed. When a plant with green peas was crossed with one with yellow peas, all of the F_1 offspring were yellow. However, when he crossed these offspring, creating what is called the second filial generation, or F_2, the resulting offspring were not all yellow. For every four offspring, three were yellow and one was green. This pattern of inheritance appeared repeatedly when Mendel tested other traits, such as pea pod shape shown in **Figure 2**. Mendel concluded that while only one form of the trait is visible in F_1, in F_2 the missing trait sometimes shows itself.

Plan It!

SEP Plan Investigations Consider five other traits that Mendel investigated. Explain how you could repeat Mendel's procedure for one of these traits and what the likely results would be of your investigation.

Trait	Dominant	Recessive
seed shape	round	wrinkled
seed color	yellow	green
pod color	green	yellow
flower color	purple	white
pod position on stem	side of stem	top of stem

....

....

....

....

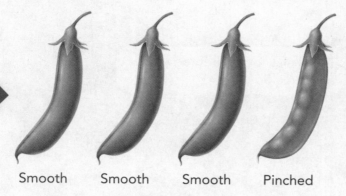

Smooth   Smooth   Smooth   Pinched

F₂ generation

HANDS-ON LAB

Investigate Explore cross-pollination by examining the parts of a flower.

Genes Affect Inheritance

In Mendel's time, people had no knowledge of genetic material or its ability to carry the code for an organism's traits. However, Mendel was still able to formulate several ideas about heredity from his experiments. He called the information that carried the traits **factors**, because they determined what was expressed. He also determined that for every trait, organisms receive one factor from their mother and one factor from their father. He concluded that one factor can mask the expression of the other even if both are present at the same time.

Different Forms of Genes
Today, the term *factor* has been replaced with *gene* or *allele*. Alleles are the different forms of a gene. Pea plants have one gene that controls the color of the seeds. This gene may be expressed as either yellow or green through a combination of yellow alleles and green alleles. When crossed, each parent donates one of its alleles for seed color to the offspring. The allele that each parent donates is random. An offspring's seed color is determined by the combination of both alleles.

An organism's traits are controlled by the alleles it inherits. A **dominant allele** is one whose trait always shows up in the organism when the allele is present. A **recessive allele**, on the other hand, is hidden whenever the dominant allele is present. If one parent donates a dominant allele and the other donates a recessive allele, only the dominant trait will be expressed.

☑ CHECK POINT **Determine Meaning** What conditions would have to occur for offspring to express the recessive trait?

....

....

Academic Vocabulary

How is *factor* used differently in math and science?

....

....

....

....

....

....

Student Discourse
Think about a time when you saw a baby animal, such as a puppy or kitten. Think about the traits it inherited from its parents. How could you determine which traits were dominant and which were recessive? Discuss the question with a classmate and record your ideas in your science notebook.

Dominant Color

Figure 3 ✏ Mendel discovered that yellow is the dominant pea seed color, while the recessive pea seed color is green. Complete the statements. Use the letters G and g as needed.

Apply Concepts What are the alleles for the green pea seed? Would it be a purebred or a hybrid?

....

....

The alleles for a purebred yellow seed would be ....

The alleles for a hybrid yellow seed would be ....

Literacy Connection

Determine Conclusions How did Mendel come to the conclusion that an organism's traits were carried on different alleles? Underline the sentence that answers this question.

Writing Gene Expression

The traits we see are present because of the combination of alleles. For example, the peas in **Figure 3** show two different colors. Pea color is the gene, while the combinations of alleles determine how the gene will be expressed. To represent this, scientists who study patterns of inheritance, called geneticists, use letters to represent the alleles. A dominant allele is represented with a capital letter (G) and a recessive allele with a lowercase letter (g). Alleles for different traits are represented with different letters.

When an organism has two of the same alleles for a trait, it is called a purebred for that trait. This would be represented as GG or gg. When the organism has one dominant allele and one recessive allele, it is called a hybrid for that trait. This would be represented as Gg. Remember that each trait is represented by two alleles, one from each parent. Depending upon which alleles are inherited, the offspring may be a purebred or a hybrid.

Mendel's work was quite revolutionary. Prior to his work, many people assumed that all traits in offspring were a mixture of each parent's traits. Mendel's experiments, where traits appeared in the F_2 generation that were not in the F_1 generation, disproved this idea.

Probability and Heredity

When you flip a coin, what are the chances it will come up heads? Because there are two options (heads or tails), the probability of getting heads is 1 out of 2. The coin has an equal chance of coming up heads or tails. Each toss has no effect on the outcome of the next toss. **Probability** is a number that describes how likely it is that an event will occur. The laws of probability predict what is likely to happen and what is not likely to happen.

Probability and Genetics
When dealing with genetics and inheritance, it is important to know the laws of probability. Every time two parents produce offspring, the probability of certain traits getting passed on is the same. For example, do you know any families that have multiple children, but all of them are the same sex? Picture a family where all the children are girls. According to the laws of probability, a boy should have been born already, but there is no guarantee of that happening. Every time these parents have a child, the probability of having a boy remains the same as the probability of having a girl.

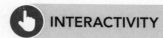

INTERACTIVITY

Explore the probability of the colors of pea plant flowers.

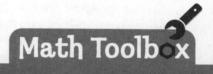
Math Toolbox

Determining Probability

Probability is an important part of the science of genetics. Answer the questions on probability below.

1. **Predict** The probability of a specific allele from one parent being passed on to an offspring is 1 in 2, or ½. This is the same probability as predicting a coin toss correctly. How often would you expect a coin to show tails if you flip it 100 times?

   ....

2. **CCC Identify Patterns** A die is a six-sided cube with dots representing the numbers 1 through 6. What is the probability of rolling a 3?

   ....

3. **Use a Probability Model** You and a friend both roll a die at the same time. On the first roll, the dots on the two dice add up to 7. On the second roll, they add up to 2. Which do you think was more likely, rolling a total of 2 or a total of 7? Explain your answer.

   ....

   ....

   ....

   ....

   ....

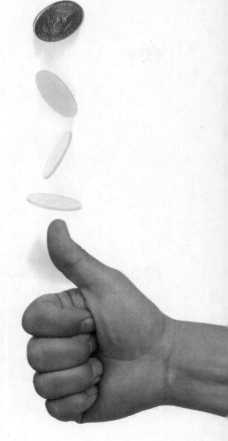

Making a Punnett Square

To determine the probability of inheriting alleles, geneticists use a model called a Punnett square. To construct a Punnett square, it is important to know what trait is being considered and whether the parents are pure-bred or hybrid.

The following steps demonstrate how to use a Punnett square to calculate the probability of offspring having different combinations of alleles. The example describes the procedure for a cross between two hybrid parents; however, this procedure will work for any cross.

Using a Punnett Square

Mendel's experiments involved crossing two hybrid pea plants in the F_1 generation. Most plants in the F_2 generation showed the dominant trait, but some showed the recessive trait. A Punnett square uses the laws of probability to demonstrate why those results occurred. Consider the question of what the offspring of two hybrid pea plants with yellow seed color will likely be.

1 **Draw a square box** divided into four square parts.

One parent's alleles go on top and the other parent's alleles go on the left.

2 **Determine the alleles** of each of the parents. You know that they are both hybrids, so they have one dominant allele (represented as a capital letter) and one recessive allele (represented as a lowercase letter). Place one set of alleles on top of the columns of the box, and one set of alleles next to the rows of the box, as shown.

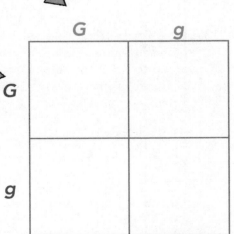

	G	g
G	GG	Gg
g	Gg	gg

3 **Do the cross!** Inside each box, combine the letter at the top of the column with the letter to the left of the row the box is in. Always write a dominant allele before a recessive allele.

4 **Determine the likelihood** of different combinations of alleles. As you can see from the Punnett square, the combination *GG* occurs ¼ of the time, the combination *Gg* occurs ²⁄₄, or ½ of the time, and the combination *gg* occurs ¼ of the time.

5 **Determine which trait is expressed** for each combination of alleles. In this example, the combination *GG* and *Gg* result in the dominant yellow seed color, while the combination *gg* results in the green seed color. Therefore, the dominant allele will be expressed ¾ of the time. This matches the results of Mendel's experiments.

SEP Use Models ✎ You cross a pea plant that is hybrid for yellow seed color (*Gg*) with a purebred green seed color (*gg*) plant. Draw a Punnett square to describe the results of the cross. What is the probability that the offspring will have green seed color?

....

Genetic Makeup and Physical Traits

You are already familiar with the terms *purebred* and *hybrid*. These terms refer to a genotype, an organism's genetic makeup or combination of alleles. As shown in **Figure 4**, the genotype of a purebred green seed pea plant would be *gg*. Both alleles are the same (purebred) and they are recessive because green is the recessive trait in terms of seed color. The hybrid genotype for this trait would be *Gg*.

The expression of an organism's genes is called its phenotype, the organism's physical appearance or visible traits. The height, the shape, the color, the size, the texture—whatever trait is being expressed, is referred to as the phenotype. So, a pea plant with the phenotype of yellow seed color could have two possible genotypes, *GG* or *Gg*.

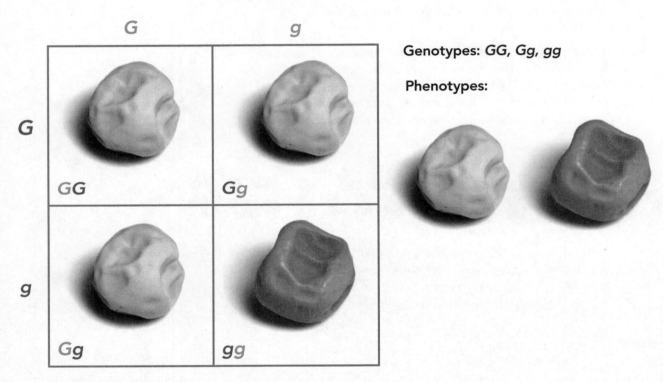

Genotypes: *GG*, *Gg*, *gg*

Phenotypes:

Describing Seed Color

Figure 4 The phenotype of an organism is explained as physical characteristics we see, while the genotype describes the combination of alleles that are inherited.

Describing Genetic Makeup There are two other terms geneticists use to describe genotypes. Instead of saying *purebred*, they refer to an organism with two identical alleles as *homozygous* (*homo*-means "the same"). When the alleles are both dominant, as in the yellow seed plant (*GG*), the genotype is called homozygous dominant. However, when the alleles are both recessive, as in the green seed color (*gg*), the genotype is called homozygous recessive. When an organism is a hybrid, as in yellow seed color (*Gg*), the genotype is called the heterozygous condition (*hetero*- means "different").

☑ CHECK POINT **Cite Textual Evidence** Is it possible for two organisms to have the same physical characteristic but have a different genetic makeup? Explain.

....

....

....

....

....

....

....

....

....

....

....

....

....

....

....

....

....

....

....

Other Patterns of Inheritance

Not all patterns of inheritance are simple. The majority of genes have more than two alleles. And the alleles for a single gene often influence multiple traits. Also, traits are usually determined by more than one gene.

Sometimes intermediate forms of a dominant trait appear. This means that mixing of colors or sizes occurs. Incomplete dominance may occur when a dominant allele and recessive allele are inherited. The offspring will have a mixture of these two alleles. Incomplete dominance can occur in petal color in some species of plants. **Figure 5** shows how petal color can result in the blending of two colors.

Incomplete Dominance
Figure 5 ✏ Circle the flowers that demonstrate incomplete dominance in petal color.

Unlike incomplete dominance, which shows blending of traits, codominance results in both alleles being expressed at the same time. This color pattern appears when a dominant white-hair allele and a dominant solid-color allele are inherited. The offspring has hairs of each color intermixed, giving the solid color a more muted or mottled look.

Every offspring inherits one allele from each parent for a total of two alleles. However, sometimes one trait has more than two alleles. For example, human blood type is on a gene with multiple alleles—A, B, and O. The A and B blood types are codominant and O is recessive. You receive two of the multiple alleles from each parent, but each possible combination of alleles results in one of four different blood types.

Some traits are controlled by more than one gene. In polygenetic inheritance, these different genes are expressed together to produce the trait. Human height is an example of this. If the mother is 5 feet 2 inches tall and the father is 6 feet tall, then you might think that all of the offspring would be 5 feet 7 inches. However, there can be a large variation among the heights of the children. This fact is due to multiple genes working together to produce the trait.

INTERACTIVITY

Explore how organisms transfer traits from parents to offspring.

☑ CHECK POINT **Determine Central Ideas** Why is it incorrect to always assume that an inherited trait is caused by a single gene or that a single gene influences a single trait?

....

....

....

....

....

Genes and the Environment

What kinds of things have you learned in your life? Maybe you know how to paint. Maybe you can ride a unicycle. Or maybe you know how to solve very complicated math problems. Whatever your abilities, they are acquired traits that are the result of learned behaviors.

Acquired Traits The traits you inherited can be affected by your experience. For example, humans are born with teeth, vocal cords, and tongues—all of which enable us to speak. The language you learn to use depends on your environment. You were not born speaking a particular language, but you were born with the capacity to learn languages, whether a spoken language or sign language. The ability for language is an inherited trait. The language or languages you use, however, are acquired traits.

The combination of inherited traits and acquired traits helps many organisms to survive in their environment. The fox squirrel in **Figure 6** has inherited traits from its parents that help it survive in its environment. The squirrel also acquired traits that help it survive, by learning behaviors from its parents and by interacting with its environment.

HANDS-ON LAB

и**Investigate** Explore traits in an imaginary organism.

Acquired Traits

Figure 6 This fox squirrel, common in the Los Angeles area in California, has traits that were inherited as well as traits that were acquired through learning.

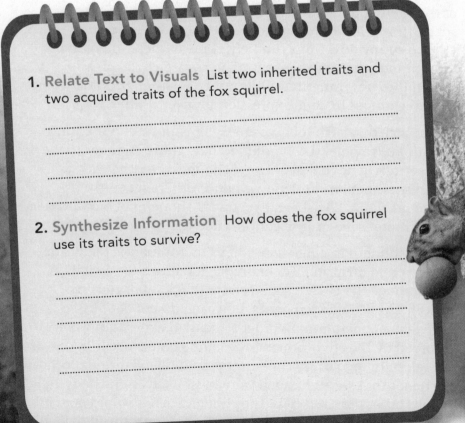

1. **Relate Text to Visuals** List two inherited traits and two acquired traits of the fox squirrel.

....
....
....
....

2. **Synthesize Information** How does the fox squirrel use its traits to survive?

....
....
....
....
....

Environmental Interactions

Figure 7 Protection from the sun when you are outside all day is important.

Implement a Solution List three acquired behaviors that people have learned to protect themselves from ultraviolet light.

....

....

....

....

Environmental Factors

Organisms interact with their environment on a regular basis. **Figure 7** shows some of the ways you interact with your environment. You may spend time with friends, breathe fresh air, exercise, and enjoy a sunny day. Unfortunately, some of these interactions may change the way a gene is expressed. Gene expression determines how inherited traits appear. The environment can lead to changes in gene expression in several ways.

Certain chemicals in tobacco smoke or exposure to the sun's harmful ultraviolet (UV) radiation may cause changes in the way certain genes behave. These changes alter the way an organism functions and may produce different traits than would normally have been expressed. Though not a guarantee, these changes may cause cancer and other diseases.

Not all changes in genes caused by environmental factors get passed on to offspring. For example, too much UV radiation can damage the DNA in skin cells to the point of causing cancer. These damaged genes, however, do not get passed to the next generation. In order to pass on genes that were changed by the environment, the change must occur in one of the sex cells—egg or sperm—that formed the offspring. Because the genes that were changed were most likely in the body cells, or cells other than sex cells, the changed genes would not be passed on to the offspring, and would affect only the individual with the changed genes.

☑ LESSON 2 Check

MS-LS3-2

1. Apply Concepts The dominant allele for dimples is *D* and the recessive allele is *d*. How would a geneticist describe the genotype of an individual with the alleles *dd*?

....

....

Use the information you calculated in the Punnett square activity to answer questions 2 and 3.

2. SEP Interpret Data How did the probabilities of yellow seeds and green seeds compare with each other?

....

....

....

....

....

....

3. CCC Cause and Effect What would happen to the probabilities of yellow and green seeds if one parent were homozygous recessive and the other were homozygous dominant? Explain.

....

....

....

....

....

....

....

4. SEP Construct an Explanation Why were Mendel's experiments with pea plants so important toward advancing current knowledge of genetics and inheritance?

....

....

....

....

....

....

....

....

5. Predict For plant stem height, the dominant allele for height is *T*, and the recessive allele is *t*. What would be the genetic makeup, physical traits, and offspring probabilities of a cross between a heterozygous parent for tall stem height and one that was homozygous recessive for short stem height?

....

....

....

....

....

....

....

....

Plant Structures for Reproduction

HANDS-ON LAB

uInvestigate Demonstrate how flower structures relate to successful reproduction.

MS-LS1-4 Use argument based on empirical evidence and scientific reasoning to support an explanation for how characteristic animal behaviors and specialized plant structures affect the probability of successful reproduction of animals and plants respectively.

Connect It!

✎ **Circle the fruits shown here.**

SEP Construct Explanations Where in the fruit are seeds found and what do seeds do?

....

....

Plant Reproduction

Have you ever run from a bee buzzing around a garden? Have you taken the time to appreciate the pleasant scent and beautiful colors of a rose? Have you challenged a friend to see who could spit a watermelon seed the farthest? If you have done any of these things, you are already familiar with some of the methods plants use to reproduce.

When a seed, like ones from the fruits in **Figure 1**, is planted in healthy soil and gets plenty of water and sunlight, it can grow into an adult plant. But this is just one part in the process of how plants reproduce. A lot must first happen in a plant's life before it can produce a seed that can grow into a plant. Surprisingly to some, plants are like animals in that reproduction requires a sperm cell fertilizing an egg cell for a new organism to begin.

Plants have evolved specialized structures over time that increase the probability of successful reproduction. Different types of plants have different structures and methods that help them reproduce. But the result is the same: producing new generations of plants.

INTERACTIVITY

Explore the relationship between seeds and the food we eat.

Find the Fruit

Figure 1 Fruits may not look alike, but they function much the same. They carry seeds with partially developed plants.

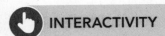
Explore how plant structures help plants reproduce asexually and sexually.

Structures for Reproduction

Over time, plants have evolved body structures that help them reproduce. Different types of plants have developed different structures in response to their environments and their unique needs. Reproduction is one of the reasons you see so much variety in the different plant types.

Asexual Reproduction Though sexual reproduction is the most common way that plants reproduce, many plants also undergo asexual reproduction. New plants can grow from the roots, leaves, or stems of a parent plant. If conditions are favorable, a single plant can quickly spread by producing many exact copies of itself. As shown in **Figure 2**, scientists can use a plant's ability to reproduce asexually in order to grow plants with favorable characteristics.

✓ CHECK POINT **Summarize Text** What is the benefit of asexual reproduction?

....

....

Apple Tree Grafting

Figure 2 Grafting is one way that humans can control the traits of plants. Part of a plant's stem is cut and then attached to another plant. These apple trees in a California orchard have been grafted to ensure that desired traits from the original plant are maintained while new desired traits from the grafted plant grow on the new stem.

Apply Concepts Is grafting a form of sexual or asexual reproduction?

....

Male and Female Cones

Figure 3 Male cones, such as the ones to the right, hold pollen. Female cones, such as the two shown below, open when the weather is warm and dry. They close when conditions are cold and wet.

Apply Scientific Reasoning How do you think the cone's ability to open and close helps with reproduction?

....
....
....
....
....

Gymnosperms Trees such as pines, redwoods, firs, cedars, and hemlocks are all classified as gymnosperms. Many gymnosperms have needle-like leaves and deep roots. However, all have cones and unprotected seeds. These two characteristics set them apart from other vascular plants. These structures allow the plants to reproduce successfully.

The structures in **Figure 3** are cones , which are the reproductive structures of gymnosperms. Male cones hold pollen, whereas the female cone has an ovule, the structure holding the egg. The female cone also makes a sticky substance on the outside of the cone, needed for pollination. Pollen from the male cone is light enough to be carried by the wind. When the wind blows, pollen may land on the sticky female cone. When this happens, the egg may become fertilized. The ovule seals off and the fertilized egg, also called a zygote, develops into a young plant, or embryo, in the seed. Seeds can remain in the female cone for a few years, until they mature.

The seeds of gymnosperms are "naked," meaning they are unprotected. Once the female cone matures, the scales open, exposing the seeds. As wind blows, the exposed seeds are blown out of the cone and spread by the wind. Having seeds that can be moved by the wind increases reproductive success because new plants may grow where the seeds land.

Literacy Connection

Cite Textual Evidence Which detail in the text helped you understand what gymnosperms are?

....
....
....
....
....
....
....

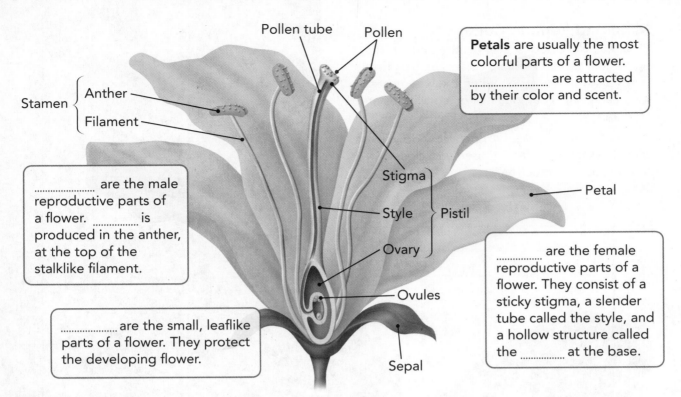

Pollen tube   Pollen

Stamen {
  Anther
  Filament
}

Petals are usually the most colorful parts of a flower. .... are attracted by their color and scent.

.... are the male reproductive parts of a flower. .... is produced in the anther, at the top of the stalklike filament.

Stigma

Style   } Pistil

Ovary

Petal

.... are the female reproductive parts of a flower. They consist of a sticky stigma, a slender tube called the style, and a hollow structure called the .... at the base.

Ovules

.... are the small, leaflike parts of a flower. They protect the developing flower.

Sepal

Flower Parts and Their Jobs

Figure 4 🖉 Flowers contain the reproductive structures of angiosperms. Complete the diagram by filling in the missing words.

CCC Relate Structure and Function How are a flower's petals important to reproduction?

....

....

....

....

....

....

HANDS-ON LAB

Investigate
Demonstrate how flower structures relate to successful reproduction.

Angiosperms All angiosperms share two important characteristics that help the plants reproduce. They all produce flowers and fruits that contain seeds. The angiosperm life cycle begins when pollen forms in the flower's anthers. These structures are found at the end of the stamens, which are the male reproductive structure. The female reproductive structure is the pistil and has three parts: the stigma, style, and ovary. When pollen falls on the stigma, pollination may occur, which can lead to fertilization.

Some angiosperms are pollinated by the wind, but most rely on animals called pollinators, such as bees, butterflies, and hummingbirds. When an organism enters a flower to obtain food, such as nectar, it becomes coated with pollen. Some of the pollen can drop onto the flower's stigma as the animal leaves. The pollen can also be brushed onto the stigma of the next flower the animal visits. If the pollen falls on the stigma of a similar plant, fertilization can occur. A sperm cell joins with an egg cell inside an ovule within the ovary at the base of the flower. The zygote then begins to develop into the seed's embryo. Other parts of the ovule develop into the rest of the seed.

Additional structures help a flowering plant to reproduce successfully. Colorful, often pleasantly-scented petals surround the plant's reproductive organs and attract pollinators. Green sepals protect the growing flower. The flower is what develops into the **fruit**—the ripened ovary and other structures of an angiosperm enclosing one or more seeds.

Seed Dispersal Fruits are the means by which angiosperm seeds are **dispersed**. Often the scent and color of fruit attracts animals to the plant. Animals eat the fruit and then the seeds in it pass through the animal's digestive system. As the animal moves around, seeds are deposited in different areas in the animal's dung, or droppings. The droppings have an added benefit of providing nutrients and moisture for the seed.

In other cases, seeds disperse by falling into water or being carried by the wind. Seeds with barbs attach to fur or clothing and are carried away. Others are ejected by the seed pods and scattered in different directions. Seeds dispersed far from the parent plant have a better chance of surviving. Distance keeps the new plant from competing with the parent plant for light, water, and nutrients. When a seed lands in a spot with suitable conditions, germination may occur. **Germination** occurs when the embryo sprouts out of the seed.

✓ CHECK POINT **Cite Textual Evidence** How do the examples of seed dispersal given in the text help you understand the role of seed dispersal in plant reproduction?

....

....

....

Academic Vocabulary
Use *dispersed* in another sentence that uses a context other than seeds and plants.

....

....

....

....

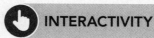 **INTERACTIVITY**

Explore the relationship between plants and pollinators.

Model It

Flower to Fruit
The male and female flower parts enable reproduction to take place. They contain structures to form the egg and sperm that will join to create the zygote.

SEP Develop Models 🖊 Draw a sequence of pictures to show the steps that must take place for a flowering plant to reproduce and form a new seedling.

MS-LS1-4

1. **Communicate** What is a fruit?

....

....

....

2. **Draw Conclusions** How are flowers with brightly-colored petals and attractive scents helpful to plants?

....

....

....

....

3. **Determine Differences** How does seed dispersal in angiosperms differ from seed dispersal in gymnosperms?

....

....

....

....

....

4. **SEP Construct Explanations** In what ways are sexual and asexual reproduction in plants similar, and in what ways do they differ?

....

....

....

....

....

....

....

....

5. **SEP Engage in Argument** A classmate tells you he read on the Internet that plants need flowers to produce seeds. Respond using evidence from this text.

....

....

....

....

....

....

Quest CHECK-IN

In this lesson, you learned about plant structures that help them reproduce successfully.

SEP Design Solutions How might knowing about the ways the local plants reproduce help in the planning and design of the basketball court?

....

....

....

....

....

INTERACTIVITY

Protect the Plants

Go online to assess the impact of the construction project on plants.

MS-LS1-5

GARDENING in Space

Do you know how to grow plants in space? You engineer it! NASA engineers and astronauts show us how.

The Challenge: To grow plants on long space flights.

Phenomenon Future space-flight missions will take months, years, and eventually multiple lifetimes, to reach their distant destinations. These missions will rely on growing plants in space as a source of food for astronauts, a method for recycling carbon dioxide into breathable oxygen, and potentially as part of the process that recycles, filters, and purifies water.

Plant structures and their functions are adapted to life on Earth. Leaves grow toward sunlight and roots grow down, due to gravity. In space, with no sunlight and very little gravity, plants do not grow easily. Because water floats away without gravity, watering plants in space is also tricky. Astronauts grow some plants directly in water. Other plants grow in a spongy clay-like material that allows water to reach all the roots.

NASA engineers have designed plant growth chambers used on the International Space Station (ISS) to investigate the effects of space on plant growth. The systems use LED lights and have multiple sensors to track data on temperature, moisture, and oxygen levels.

INTERACTIVITY

Learn more about growing plants in space.

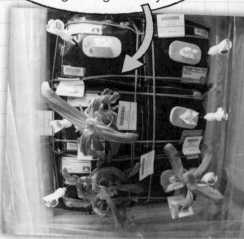

This is not a picture taken from above. These plants are growing sideways!

The Veggie System was installed in 2014. It allows the astronauts to grow their own food aboard the ISS.

DESIGN CHALLENGE

Can you design and build a model of a lunar growth chamber for plants? Go to the Engineering Design Notebook to find out!

Animal Behaviors for Reproduction

HANDS-ON LAB

ηInvestigate Explore how salmon migrate from the ocean back to their home river.

MS-LS1-4 Use argument based on empirical evidence and scientific reasoning to support an explanation for how characteristic animal behaviors and specialized plant structures affect the probability of successful reproduction of animals and plants respectively.

Connect It !

🖊 **Circle a vulnerable member of this wood duck family.**

SEP Construct Explanations Why do you think the ducks travel this way?

....

....

Animal Behavior

Have you ever noticed how busy animals are? Most are constantly looking for food or trying to avoid other animals that think of them as food. Many also spend a lot of time looking for mates and caring for their young. All of these actions are examples of an animal's behavior. The way an organism reacts to changes in its internal conditions or external environment is **behavior**. Like body structures, the behaviors of animals are adaptations that have developed over long periods of time.

Some behaviors are learned while others are known without being taught. An **instinct** is a response to a stimulus that is inborn and that an animal performs correctly the first time. For example, when sea turtles hatch from their eggs, they know by instinct to travel to the ocean. Other behaviors are learned. Learning is the process that leads to changes in behavior based on practice or experience.

The goal of most animal behaviors is to help them survive or reproduce (**Figure 1**). When an animal looks for food or hides from a predator, it is doing something that helps it stay alive. When animals search for mates and build nests for their young, they are behaving in ways that help them reproduce.

HANDS-ON LAB

Consider how animals can communicate without words.

Wood Duck Behavior

Figure 1 These wood ducklings on Lindo Lake in Lakeside, California, stay close to their mother for protection.

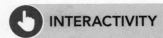

INTERACTIVITY

Find out more about animal behavior.

Literacy Connection

Summarize Text After reading each section of text, briefly summarize the key ideas from that section to a family member or classmate or make an audio recording of yourself. Later, go back and listen to the recording or play it for someone else. Clarify any ideas that may be confusing.

Mating Behaviors When animals mate, a male animal fertilizes a female animal's egg cells with his sperm cells. The fertilized egg will eventually develop into a new organism. This process is an important part of ensuring the continued survival of the species. Scientists believe that the drive to reproduce evolved in animals over time as a way to ensure the success of their species and their own individual genes.

The behavior patterns related to how animals mate are called **mating systems**, and they vary from species to species. Some species of animals are monogamous. That means that they only mate with one other organism for a period of time, which can range from just a season or to their entire lives. In other animal species, such as baboons, a male has multiple female mates at one time. There are other species in which females have multiple male mates. Honeybees use this mating system. In still other species, males and females both have multiple mates during any one period of time. Scientists believe that these different mating systems evolved over time to best meet the needs of each particular species.

Model It

The terms defined below are used to describe the different mating systems that are observed in animal species.

monogamy: one female mates with one male
polygyny: one male mates with multiple females
polyandry: one female mates with multiple males
polygynandry: females mate with multiple males and males mate with multiple females

SEP Develop Models 🖉 Use the information above and the symbols for male and female, which are shown to the right, to model the four types of mating systems in the space provided. Monogamy has been completed for you.

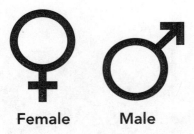

Female   Male

Monogamy

Locking Horns
Figure 2 Bighorn sheep are found in the mountains and deserts of southeastern California. These male bighorns display aggression as they compete for mates.

Explain Phenomena What is the goal of this competitive behavior?

....

....

....

....

....

Imagine a male walrus swimming in the icy water making a series of whistling and clacking sounds. A group of females looks on from the floating ice pack. One joins the male in the water and they dive together in a dance-like ritual. This is an example of a courtship behavior, an activity that prepares males and females of the same species for mating. These behaviors are ways for animals to attract the attention of potential mates.

Communication
Animals communicate in many ways, using sounds, scents, and body movements. Often, the goal of communication is reproduction.

One way animals communicate is with sound. You have probably heard birds singing outside. Birds communicate with sound for many reasons, but mainly they sing to attract mates. Many animals also use chemical scents to send messages. A chemical released by one animal that affects the behavior of another animal of the same species is called a **pheromone** (fehr uh mohn). In many species of moths, for example, females release a pheromone into the air that is a signal to males that she is ready to mate.

Competition
Animals compete for resources, such as food and water. They also compete for access to mates, which may involve displays of aggression (**Figure 2**). Aggression is a threatening behavior that one animal uses to intimidate or dominate another animal. Another competitive behavior that is often observed in animals is establishing and maintaining a territory. A territory is an area that is occupied and defended by an animal or group of animals. An animal that is defending its territory will drive away other animals that may compete with it for mates.

Reflect As you learn about animal behaviors related to reproduction, spend some time observing animals in the area around your neighborhood and school. Record notes and observations in your science notebook. Explain what type of behavior you think you were observing and why.

Parental Investment

Different animal species have different ways of caring for their young. Some species have no contact with their offspring, while others spend many years caring for them.

Without Parental Help

Most amphibian larvae, or tadpoles, develop into adults without parental help. Similarly, the offspring of most reptiles, such as snakes, are independent from the time they hatch. Offspring that do not receive parental care must be able to care for themselves from the time of birth. Generally, animals that provide no parental care release many eggs at a time. Although many will not survive, the sheer number of potential offspring ensures that at least some will survive and later reproduce.

With Parental Help

The offspring of most birds and all mammals typically spend weeks to years under the care and protection of a parent. Most bird species lay eggs in nests that one or both parents build. Then one or both parents sit on the eggs, keeping them warm until they hatch. After hatching, one or both parents will feed and protect their young until they are able to care for themselves.

Young mammals, such as the infant chimpanzee in **Figure 3**, are usually quite helpless for a long time after they are born. After birth, mammals are fed with milk from the mother's body. One or both parents may continue caring for their offspring until the young animals are independent. Typically, animals that provide parental care have only a few offspring at a time. Many only have one. Scientists believe that these animals work harder to care for their young because they have fewer or no other offspring to take their place.

Academic Vocabulary

What are some synonyms, or words and phrases that have a similar meaning, for the term *typically*?

....

....

....

Parenting Behavior
Figure 3 This female chimpanzee carries her infant on her back until it is old enough to better care for itself.

CCC Cause and Effect What are the benefits and drawbacks of this behavior for the mother chimpanzee?

....

....

....

....

....

....

....

Survivorship Curves

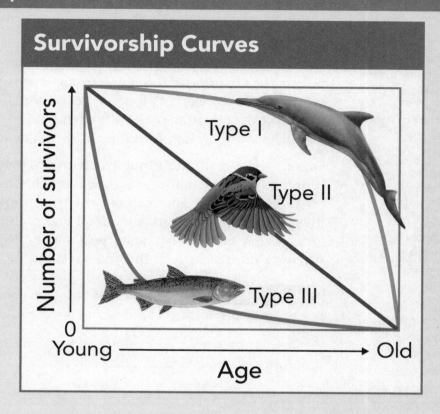

Survivorship Curves

Number of survivors

Type I

Type II

Type III

0

Young ⟶ Old

Age

To show how the probability of death changes with age for different species, scientists use graphs called survivorship curves. In a Type I survivorship curve, individuals are most likely to live a full life. In a Type III survivorship curve, individuals are most likely to die when they are young. In a Type II survivorship curve, an individual's chance of dying remains constant.

Draw Comparative Inferences What can you infer about the role of parental care for the three species represented in the graph? How does this relate to reproductive success in each species?

....
....
....
....
....
....
....
....
....

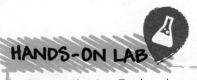

HANDS-ON LAB

Investigate Explore how salmon migrate from the ocean back to their home river.

INTERACTIVITY

Consider the impact of light pollution on an animals' mating behaviors.

Student Discourse

With a partner, debate the benefits of working alone vs. working on a team. Each take one side, listing the benefits of your side and an argument for each. Take turns sharing your arguments. Then, each partner will refute (argue against) any arguments or to add a benefit your partner did not think of.

Working Together

Figure 4 Orcas live in a group called a pod. All adults in the pod help parent any offspring. Likewise, some spiders live in a nest and work together to raise all young.

CCC Cause and Effect

What are the benefits of shared responsibility when raising young? Explain.

....
....
....
....
....
....

Cooperative Behaviors

In some cases, animals increase their chances for surviving and reproducing when they live and work together. For example, some fish form schools, and some insects live in large groups. Hoofed mammals, such as bison and wild horses, often form herds. Living in a group helps these animals stay alive.

One benefit of living in a large group is that it is an effective way to protect young animals from predators. Elephants protect the offspring of the group by forming a defensive circle around them. By working together, each adult female helps to protect the offspring of the other females. In turn, the other members of the group protect her offspring as well.

Other species of animals that live in groups may take on parenting responsibilities of animals that are not their offspring (**Figure 4**). For example, there are worker bees in a hive whose sole job is providing food and protection for the bee larvae. They may not be the parents of the offspring, but they still work hard to care for the hive's young.

CHECK POINT **Summarize Text** How can cooperative behaviors help animals that are raising offspring?

....
....
....
....
....

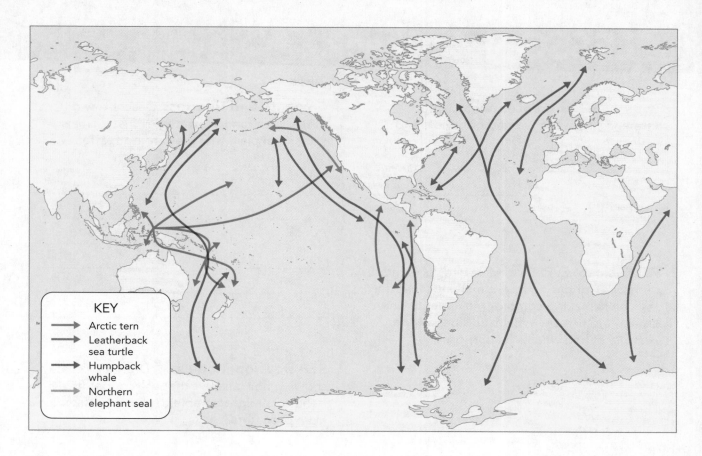

KEY
→ Arctic tern
→ Leatherback sea turtle
→ Humpback whale
→ Northern elephant seal

Migratory Behaviors Many animals spend their entire lives in a relatively small area. But there are many others that migrate. **Migration** is the regular, seasonal journey of an animal from one place to another and back again. Animals have different reasons for migration. Some migrate to an area that provides plenty of food or a more comfortable climate during a harsh season. Others, such as the animals whose migratory routes are shown in **Figure 5**, migrate to a better environment for reproduction. In some cases, large groups of animals of the same species gather together in the same place at the same time so they can mate. They may also stay there to begin the process of raising their young. By migrating every year, these animals increase their chances of finding a mate and producing offspring in conditions that will be favorable to their survival.

Animal behaviors related to mating and raising offspring are often tied to Earth's cycles. Polar bears, for example, mate in the spring and give birth in the winter. Other animals reproduce with more or less frequency, but almost all follow some kind of predictable cycle. Following these patterns ensures that off-spring are born when they have the best chances of survival.

Migratory Routes

Figure 5 Many animals travel thousands of miles every year to mate and raise their young.

SEP Use Models 🖊 A friend took a road trip across the United States from the west coast to the east coast. Draw an arrow on the map showing the trip. How does your friend's trip compare to the animal trips represented in the map?

....

....

....

....

MS-LS1-4

1. Determine Differences What is the difference between learned behaviors and instincts?

....
....
....
....

2. SEP Evaluate Evidence Male birds of paradise are known for having bright markings that they flash while making complex movements when females are nearby. What is this behavior an example of and what is its purpose?

....
....
....
....

3. SEP Construct Explanations Describe how animals use pheromones to attract potential mates.

....
....
....
....
....

4. Compare and Contrast Describe two different parenting strategies that animals use and explain why they are both effective.

....
....
....
....
....
....
....
....

5. SEP Develop Models ✐ Draw a picture showing how animals that use cooperative behaviors might be able to protect offspring from predators.

Quest CHECK-IN

In this lesson, you learned how animal behaviors can help individuals find mates. You also learned how animal parenting behaviors can affect how likely their offspring are to survive.

Explain Phenomena Consider various ways a male bird might attract a female mate. Suppose the male bird is of a species that does not display colorful feathers. What sort of behaviors could the male birds use to attract female birds?

....
....
....

👆 INTERACTIVITY

The Mating Game

Go online to explore different techniques and behaviors that animals use to increase their odds of reproductive success.

 MS-LS1-4

Avian Artists

As male birds go, the Vogelkop bowerbird is rather plain. It doesn't have the bright feathers of a cardinal or the fancy plumage of a peacock. But what the bowerbird lacks in color, it makes up for in engineering and decorating skills.

The Vogelkop bowerbird displays some of the most complex courtship behavior observed in birds. To attract a mate, the male builds an elaborate structure out of twigs, called a bower. After completing the bower, the male bowerbird collects brightly colored flowers and berries to decorate the bower. Males compete to build the most magnificent bowers and amass the most beautiful collections in the hopes of impressing female bowerbirds.

When a female comes by to inspect the bower and collection, the male will strut and sing inside the bower. If the female likes the male's decorating expertise, then they will mate. The female will leave to build a nest and raise the young on her own.

MY DISCOVERY

What other animal species display extraordinary behavior when it comes to courtship? Do some research to find out more.

Male Vogelkop bowerbirds spend years making their bowers.

The Vogelkop bowerbird lives on the island of New Guinea in the Pacific Ocean.

5 Factors Influencing Growth

HANDS-ON LAB

иInvestigate Observe how environmental factors such as pollution affect plant growth.

MS-LS1-5 Construct a scientific explanation based on evidence for how environmental and genetic factors influence the growth of organisms.

Connect It!

✏️ **These palm trees grow in the desert. Circle a part of the palm tree that helps it survive in the dry conditions of the desert.**

SEP Construct Explanations How do you think this part of the tree helps it to stay alive in the desert?

....

....

Growth and Development of Organisms

The way organisms grow and develop, and the size they reach, varies from species to species.

Several factors influence how organisms grow. Some are determined by the genetic characteristics that are passed from parent to offspring during reproduction. Other factors occur outside of the organism and can be related to their access to needed resources, the conditions in their environment, and their responses to other **stimuli**. Healthy plants inherit traits that determine successful growth, but if the conditions around them are not ideal, the plants may not grow or develop normally.

Plants and animals have changed over time. These changes are a result of adapting to the stimuli of environmental factors. These adaptations have increased their odds for survival. The palm trees in **Figure 1**, for example, have evolved to survive dry desert conditions. Dried leaves create thick fronds that shade the tree's trunk to prevent it from losing moisture.

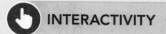

INTERACTIVITY

Explore the conditions required for living things to grow and thrive.

HANDS-ON LAB

Investigate Analyze and explain how genetic factors affect the growth of adult plants.

Academic Vocabulary

Often, a dog barks when someone rings the doorbell and knocks on the door. What are the stimuli in this situation?

....

....

....

Plant Growth
Figure 1 These California fan palms are adapted to the dry conditions of Indian Gorge in San Diego County.

Plant Responses and Growth

If you've ever grown a garden, you've probably witnessed how plants grow over time. As with all living things, plant growth is controlled by responses to the stimuli of local environmental factors. For plants, these responses are controlled by **hormones**, chemicals that affect growth and development. One important plant hormone is called **auxin** (AWK sin). It speeds up the rate at which plant cells grow and controls a plant's response to light.

Tropisms

In animals, a typical response to a stimulus is to move toward or away from it. But plants cannot move in the same way that animals do, so they often respond by growing either toward or away from a stimulus. A plant's growth response toward or away from a stimulus is called a **tropism** (TROH piz um). Touch, gravity, and light are three stimuli that trigger tropisms in plants.

The stems of some plants, such as the vines, show a response to touch called thigmotropism. As a vine grows, it coils around any object it touches. This is an example of positive thigmotropism, because the vine grows toward the stimulus. Plants also know which direction to grow, because they respond to gravity. This response is called gravitropism. Roots show positive gravitropism if they grow downward. Stems, on the other hand, show negative gravitropism (**Figure 2**). Plants' response to light is called phototropism. The leaves, stems, and flowers of plants grow toward light.

How Plants Respond
Figure 2 Plants respond to local environmental factors in a variety of ways.

Negative Gravitropism The stems of plants respond to the stimulus of gravity by growing upward, away from gravity.

CCC Cause and Effect How does gravitropism affect the growth of a plant?

Positive Phototropism When stems and leaves grow toward sources of light, they show positive phototropism.

CCC Patterns 🖊 Place an arrow pointing to where the sun would be in the picture above.

....

....

Seasonal Change Depending on where you live, you may have noticed flowers blooming in the spring and the leaves of trees changing color in autumn. These changes are caused by changing conditions brought on by the seasons.

In many plants, the amount of darkness they experience determines when they bloom. A plant's response to seasonal changes in the length of night and day is called photoperiodism. As shown in **Figure 2**, plants respond differently to night length. Other plants are not affected at all by the lengths of days and nights.

Have you ever wondered why some trees lose their leaves in the fall? As winter draws near, many plants prepare to go into a state of **dormancy**. Dormancy is a period when an organism's growth or activity stops. Dormancy helps plants survive freezing temperatures and the lack of liquid water. With many trees, the first visible change is that the leaves begin to turn color. Cooler weather and shorter days cause the leaves to stop making chlorophyll. As chlorophyll breaks down, yellow and orange pigments become visible. This causes the brilliant colors of autumn leaves like the ones shown in **Figure 2**. Over the next few weeks, sugar and water are transported out of the tree's leaves. When the leaves fall to the ground, the tree is ready for winter.

Photoperiodism Irises, left, bloom when days are getting longer and nights are getting shorter. Chrysanthemums, above, bloom when the lengths of the day and night reach a certain ratio.

Dormancy Some species of trees go into a state of dormancy every winter.

Analyze Benefits Why do you think some trees evolved to go into a state of dormancy during the winter months?

....

....

....

Plant Diseases

Figure 3 Insects, worms, and other pests can cause disease in plants and have an impact on their growth.

Make Observations ✏️ Circle the diseased parts of the plant.

📓 **Write About It** Locate two plants in or around your home, school, or neighborhood: one that appears healthy and one that does not. Explain which factors you think are helping the healthy plant grow and which factors are keeping the unhealthy one from growing to its full size.

Environmental Conditions

In ideal conditions, a plant will reach a certain maximum size that is normal for its species. However, in some cases, plants do not get enough of the resources they need, so they do not grow as large as they normally would. A lack of sunlight, for instance, may keep a plant from growing to full size or weaken its structure.

In addition to sunlight, plants need nutrient-rich soil and water to grow. Soil contains the nutrients a plant needs to carry out its life processes. Nutrient-poor soil may result from an area being overly crowded with plants. Competition for the nutrients in the soil may mean that few plants get the nutrients they need. Similarly, if a plant does not receive enough water, it will not grow to a healthy size. Diseases like the one shown in **Figure 3** can impact plant growth as well.

Plan It!

Water Needs and Plant Growth

SEP Plan Your Investigation You want to find out how the amount of water you give plants affects their growth. In the space below, describe a plan for an investigation that can help you answer this question.

....

....

....

....

....

....

....

Animal Growth

Like plants, animals grow and develop. Also like plants, their growth is affected by both internal and external stimuli to which they are constantly responding.

External and Internal Factors Animal growth and development are affected by both internal and external factors. Internal factors include genetic and hormonal characteristics that are part of an organism's life processes. External factors, on the other hand, are the environmental conditions that an animal may or may not have any control over.

Environmental Conditions Access to resources and exposure to diseases and parasites can also affect the growth and development of animals. If animals do not receive the nutrition they need during development or if they become sick, they may not reach their full adult size. Space is another resource that can affect animal growth. For example, the growth of some species of fish, such as goldfish like the one in **Figure 4**, is affected by how large a body of water they live in. If its living space is not large enough, it will not reach its full adult size.

✓ CHECK POINT **Determine Meaning** Do animals have control of the internal and external factors that affect their growth and development? Explain.

....

....

....

....

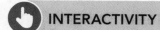

INTERACTIVITY

Observe how animals grow and develop over time.

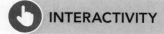

INTERACTIVITY

Find out how cows are being bred to be bigger and bigger.

Figure 4 If a goldfish's tank is too small, its growth may be restricted.

Draw Conclusions In ideal conditions, a goldfish will grow to be about 10 to 20 cm long. But most people think of goldfish as very small fish that only grow to be a few centimeters long. What conclusion can you draw from this information?

....

....

....

....

....

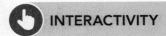
INTERACTIVITY

Observe the effects that water and food have on the growth and production of crop plants.

Genes The genes an offspring inherits from its parents are a major factor in how it develops and grows. In your own classroom, you can probably observe how students' heights vary. Part of these differences is due to the genes your classmates inherited from their parents. Children sometimes grow up to be about the same height as their parents.

Hormones Another internal factor that influences growth and development are the hormones that are naturally produced by animals' bodies. For instance, male animals produce greater amounts of testosterone than female animals. In many animal species, the production of testosterone in male animals results in males growing to be larger than females.

Math Toolbox

Human Malnutrition and Height

In 1945, after World War II, the Korean Peninsula was divided into two nations: North Korea and South Korea. The two countries had different forms of government and economic systems. The data table shows the average heights in the two countries from 1930 to 1996.

1. **Represent Quantitative Relationships** ✏ Use the data in the table to make a bar graph in the space below.

2. **Synthesize Information** Are the height differences in these two countries likely the result of genetics, hormones, or environmental conditions? Explain why.

....
....
....
....
....
....
....
....
....
....
....

Years	Average height of North Koreans (cm)	Average height of South Koreans (cm)
1930–1939	159.4	158.9
1940–1949	160.6	161.1
1950–1959	161.8	163.1
1960–1969	162.7	165
1970–1979	163.5	166.7
1980–1989	164.5	167.8
1990–1996	165.2	168.4

Source: NCD Risk Factor Collaboration, 2017

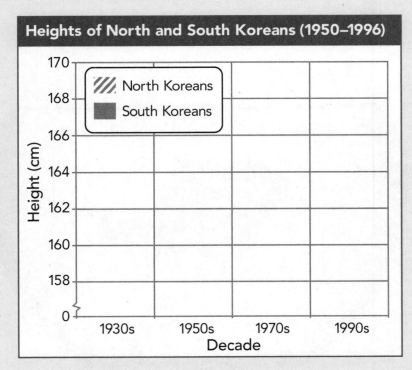

Heights of North and South Koreans (1950–1996)

☑ LESSON 5 Check

1. **Distinguish Relationships** Describe three types of stimuli that cause plants to exhibit tropism.

....

....

....

....

....

....

2. **CCC Cause and Effect** What causes plants to bloom in different seasons?

....

....

....

....

....

....

....

3. **SEP Construct Explanations** Why might soil have an effect on plant growth?

....

....

....

....

....

....

....

....

....

....

....

....

....

....

....

....

Quest CHECK-IN

In this lesson, you learned about some of the factors that affect the growth and development of plants and animals. You also learned about some of the different stages that animals go through as they develop.

SEP Design Solutions Consider the environmental impact of new construction near a wildlife habitat. At what point during the year do you think construction would have the least impact? Explain.

....

....

....

....

INTERACTIVITY

Make Your Construction Case

Go online to consider the criteria and constraints involved in your construction project.

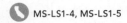

MS-LS1-4, MS-LS1-5

Evidence-Based Assessment

A team of researchers investigated how climate change and warming temperatures affected animals in the Rocky Mountains. One of the animals they studied was the yellow-bellied marmot. This large rodent lives in small colonies and survives the harsh, snowy winters by hibernating for eight months. The marmots forage for grasses and seeds, which only grow once the winter snow has melted.

Because the ground is bare of snow for such a brief time each year, the marmots have a very short breeding season. It begins as soon as they come out of hibernation. Not long after, the snow melts and more food becomes available to the marmots.

However, the researchers discovered that warming temperatures were disrupting marmot hibernation patterns even before the snow began to melt enough to provide access to food. They compiled data about the first marmot sighted coming out of hibernation each year for over 20 years. The data are summarized in the graph.

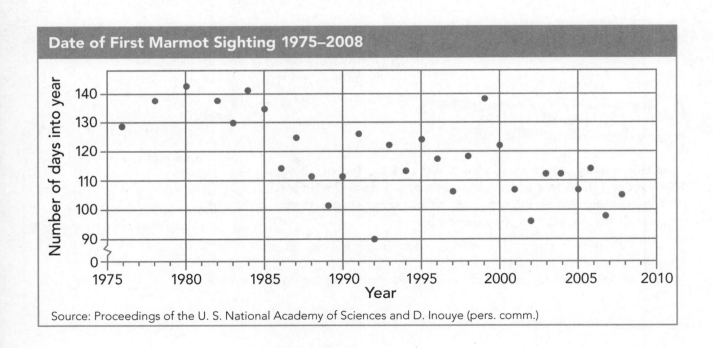

Date of First Marmot Sighting 1975–2008

Source: Proceedings of the U. S. National Academy of Sciences and D. Inouye (pers. comm.)

1. **SEP Analyze Data** What trend is shown by the data in the graph?

   A. The first marmot coming out of hibernation tends to be sighted earlier and earlier.

   B. The first marmot coming out of hibernation was sighted later each year.

   C. The date the first marmot came out of hibernation fluctuated randomly.

   D. There was little or no change in the date the first marmot was sighted each year.

2. **SEP Engage in Argument** What environmental factor do you think influences when marmots wake from hibernation? Provide support.

   ....
   ....
   ....
   ....
   ....
   ....

3. **CCC Cause and Effect** How does the marmot's behavior after coming out of hibernation increase the probability that it will successfully reproduce?

   ....
   ....
   ....
   ....
   ....
   ....

4. **Construct Arguments** What effect might an earlier breeding season have on the growth of young marmots? Select all that apply.

   ☐ Food will be abundant for young marmots.

   ☐ Fewer young marmots will be able to reproduce later.

   ☐ It will be too cold for young marmots to survive.

   ☐ Some young marmots may not grow properly.

   ☐ Some young marmots might starve.

5. **SEP Construct Explanations** The researchers found that while the air temperature is tending to increase earlier, the snow is not melting earlier. The marmots were waking up but struggling to find food. Why aren't the marmots waking up when the snow melts, instead of when the temperature warms?

   ....
   ....
   ....
   ....
   ....
   ....
   ....
   ....

Quest FINDINGS

Complete the Quest!

Finalize and present your construction plan using the information you have gathered as evidence to support your recommendations.

Apply Concepts Is there a way your town or city could ensure that the wild plants and animals that live there have the resources they need to grow and reproduce?

....
....
....
....
....

👆 **INTERACTIVITY**

Reflect on Your Basketball Court Plans

uDemonstrate Lab

MS-LS1-5, EP&CIVb

Clean and Green

How can you evaluate claims about laundry detergents that are marketed as safe for the environment?

Background

Phenomenon Many businesses promote products, such as soaps and detergents, that are environmentally friendly. *Greenwashing*, which is a combination of the terms *green* and *whitewashing*, is the practice of claiming that a product is more environmentally safe than it really is. You are a budding botanist working with an environmental watchdog group. You must evaluate the biological effects of "natural" detergents that claim to be safer for the environment than regular detergents.

In this investigation, you will design and conduct an experiment to determine the effects of "eco-friendly" laundry detergents on plant growth. It will probably take several days for the seeds to germinate. Keep in mind that the factors for healthy plant growth include height, color, and general appearance.

(per group)

- 3 plastic petri dishes with lids
- potting soil
- graduated cylinder
- 30 radish seeds
- masking tape
- day-old tap water
- metric ruler
- wax pencil
- "regular" detergent solution
- "eco-friendly" detergent solution
- scale or balance

Be sure to follow all safety guidelines provided by your teacher. The Safety Appendix of your textbook provides more details about the safety icons.

Design Your Investigation

1. With your group, discuss how you will investigate the effects of the detergents on plant growth. Also, discuss the types of data you will need to collect in order to determine how environmental factors affect plant growth.

2. Work together to identify the factors you will control and the variables you will change. Think about what a plant normally needs from its environment in order to live and grow. Decide what measurements and observations you will need to make and how often you will need to make them. To make these decisions, consider the following questions:

   • How many different groups of seeds will you use?
   • How will you determine the number of seeds that germinate in each group?
   • How will you determine the health of the shoots in each group of seeds?
   • What qualitative observations will you make?

3. Write a detailed procedure for your experiment in the space provided. Make sure you describe the setup for your investigation, the variables you will measure, a description of the data you will collect, and how you will collect the data. Before proceeding, obtain your teacher's approval.

4. In the space provided, construct a data table to organize the data you will collect. When constructing your data table, consider the following questions:

   • How many seeds will you put in each petri dish?
   • How many times will you collect data?
   • Will you collect data at the same time each day, or at different times?
   • What qualitative observations will you record?

5. Carry out your procedure for investigating the effect of your pollutant on plant growth. You will need to make observations once a day over several days. Make your measurements each day and record the data you collect.

Procedure

....
....
....
....
....
....
....
....
....
....
....

Data Table and Observations

Analyze and Interpret Data

1. **SEP Use Mathematics** Identify the dependent variables you measured in this investigation. Calculate the percentage of seeds that had germinated each day in each dish. Then, calculate the mean length of the shoots for each day you collected data. Make this calculation for the seeds in each dish.

....

....

....

....

2. **CCC Cause and Effect** Describe any patterns you see in the data for the seedlings grown under the three conditions in the petri dishes. Summarize the data by writing a cause-and-effect statement about the effects of the detergents on the growth of the plants.

....

....

....

....

....

3. **Make Generalizations** Based on the results of your experiment, do you think the manufacturer's claim is valid? Is the product safe for the long-term health of the environment? Explain.

....

....

....

....

....

4. **Compare Data** Share your results among the groups that tested the other "natural" detergents. Look for similarities and differences in the data. What do you think might account for any differences?

....

....

....

....

....

Genes and Heredity

Investigative Phenomenon
How can you use models to describe
how changes to genes may affect
organisms?

MS-LS3-1 Develop and use a model to describe why structural changes to genes (mutations) located on chromosomes may affect proteins and may result in harmful, beneficial, or neutral effects to the structure and function of the organism.

MS-LS4-4 Construct an explanation based on evidence that describes how genetic variations of traits in a population increase some individuals' probability of surviving and reproducing in a specific environment.

MS-LS4-5 Gather and synthesize information about the technologies that have changed the way humans influence the inheritance of desired traits in organisms.

EP&CIIa Students should be developing an understanding that direct and indirect changes to natural systems due to the growth of human populations and their consumption rates influence the geographic.

EP&CIIc Students should be developing an understanding that the expansion and operation of human communities influences the geographic extent, composition, biological diversity, and viability of natural systems.

How can a black bear family have different colored bears?

What questions do you have about the phenomenon?

Chromosomes and Inheritance

HANDS-ON LAB

uInvestigate Investigate genetic crosses in imaginary creatures.

MS-LS3-1 Develop and use a model to describe why structural changes to genes (mutations) located on chromosomes may affect proteins and may result in harmful, beneficial, or neutral effects to the structure and function of the organism.

Connect It!

✏️ **Circle the traits that are similar between the parents and the offspring.**

Apply Concepts How were the traits transferred from the parents to the ducklings during reproduction? Where were those traits found?

....

....

....

SEP Construct Explanations Each duckling came from these parents. They look similar, but they are not exactly the same. Why are they not identical? Explain.

....

....

Chromosomes and Genes

Gregor Mendel's ideas about inheritance and probability can be applied to all living things. Mendel determined that traits are inherited using pieces of information that he called factors and we call genes. He observed and experimented with genes in pea plants. He discovered how genes, such as those in ducks (**Figure 1**), were transferred from parents to offspring and how they made certain traits appear. However, Mendel did not know what genes actually look like.

Today, scientists know that genes are segments of code that appear on structures called **chromosomes**. These thread-like **structures** within a cell's nucleus contain DNA that is passed from one generation to the next. The genetic material of chromosomes is condensed and wrapped around special proteins. These provide support for the chromosome structure.

Chromosomes are made in the beginning of the series of events in which a cell grows, prepares for division, and divides into two new cells. During this time, the chromosome gets its characteristic *X* shape.

HANDS-ON LAB

Investigate genetic crosses in imaginary creatures.

Academic Vocabulary

Identify and describe something that has a particular structure.

....

....

....

....

....

Parents Pass Traits to Their Offspring
Figure 1 Each baby mallard duck receives some traits from the mother and some from the father.

Scales of Genetic Material

Figure 2 ✏ Order the structures from smallest to largest by writing the numbers 1 through 5 in the blank circles. Number 1 is the smallest.

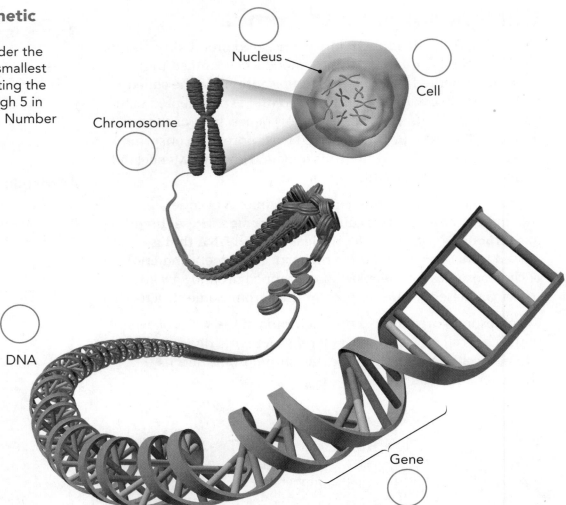

Nucleus

Cell

Chromosome

DNA

Gene

📓 **Make Meaning** Why do sex cells contain only half the number of chromosomes needed for offspring? In your science notebook, explain what would happen if sex cells contained the same number of chromosomes as body cells.

Academic Vocabulary

Your facial features are visible cues to others. They help you express, or show, your emotions. How does this relate to the way genes are expressed?

....

....

....

....

....

Number of Chromosomes Every cell in your body, other than the sex cells, has the same number of chromosomes. In humans, this number is 46. Other organisms have different numbers of chromosomes, and there is a great variety. For example, mallard ducks have 80 chromosomes. All sexually-reproducing organisms form sex cells, which have half the number of chromosomes that body cells have.

Genes on Chromosomes Every living thing needs instructions to live. Without these instructions, living things would not be able to grow and function. These instructions are located on genes. As you can see in **Figure 2,** genes are located on chromosomes. Genes are **expressed** as traits in organisms, such as hair color.

In humans, between 20,000 and 25,000 genes are found on the 46 chromosomes. Chromosomes are different sizes. Larger chromosomes contain more genes than smaller chromosomes. Each gene contains instructions for coding a particular trait. There are hundreds to thousands of genes coding traits on any given chromosome. For many organisms, these chromosomes come in sets.

Chromosome Pairs During fertilization, you receive 23 chromosomes from your father and 23 chromosomes from your mother. These chromosomes come in pairs, called homologous chromosomes, that contain the same genes. Recall that different forms of a gene are called alleles. Two alleles—one from the mother and one from the father—represent each trait. However, the alleles for these genes may or may not be the same. Some of the alleles for how the gene is expressed may be dominant or recessive. In **Figure 3**, the offspring that received these chromosomes inherited two different forms of some genes—for example, allele *A* from one parent and allele *a* from the other. The individual will be heterozygous for that gene trait. Because more than one gene is present on the 23 pairs of chromosomes, there is a wide variety of allele combinations.

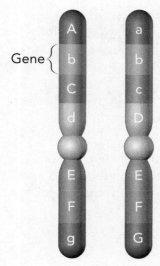

Gene

Chromosome pair

A Pair of Chromosomes
Figure 3 ✎ Circle all the pairs of alleles that would be homozygous for a trait.

✅CHECK POINT **Integrate with Visuals** How would geneticists—people who study genes—know whether the organism in **Figure 3** is homozygous or heterozygous for a certain trait by examining the chromosome pair?

....

....

....

....

Math Toolbox

Counting on Chromosomes

1. **SEP Model with Mathematics** ✎ Fill in the table with the appropriate chromosome number for the missing body cell or sex cell.

Organisms	Number of Chromosomes	
	Body Cells	Sex Cells
House cat	38	
Mallard duck		40
Corn	20	
Peanut	40	
Horse		32
Oak tree		12
Sweet potato	90	
Camel		35
Chicken	78	

2. **Construct Graphs** ✎ Complete the line plot below. Place an *X* for each organism whose body cell chromosome number falls within the given range.

Body Cell Chromosome Distribution

0–20　21–40　41–60　61–80　81–100
Number of Chromosomes

Tracking Traits

Figure 4 ✏ Sickle cell anemia is a recessive genetic disease in humans that changes the structure of red blood cells. In the pedigree, affected members are shaded.

1. **Claim** Circle couples on the pedigree who are clearly both carriers for the trait.

2. **Evidence** What is your proof?

....

....

3. **Reasoning** Explain how your evidence supports your claim.

....

....

....

....

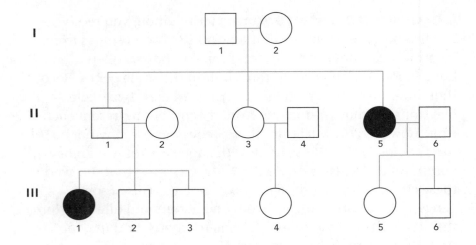

Using a Pedigree

Alelles can sometimes recombine to produce traits that are not favorable, such as a genetic disease. Geneticists study how traits are inherited in order to trace their genetic origin and predict how they may be passed on to future generations.

A pedigree is a model that geneticists use to map out the inheritance of traits. The diagram shows the presence or absence of a trait according to the relationships within a family across several generations. It is like a family tree. **Figure 4** shows multiple generations represented by Roman numerals I, II, and III. Most pedigrees show which family members express a particular trait (shaded figures). Some pedigrees also show the individuals who carry the trait but do not express it (half-shaded figures). In a pedigree, males are represented with squares and females with circles. One horizontal line connects the parent couple and another line leads down from the parents to their children.

Model It !

SEP Develop Models ✏ Think of a trait that you admire. How can that trait get passed through a family? Create a pedigree that outlines the transmission of this trait through a family. Consider who has the trait, who is a carrier for it, and who does not have it.

Forming Sex Cells

In organisms that reproduce sexually, a body cell has twice as many chromosomes as a sex cell. Why is this important? Well, it is through the sex cells that parents pass their genes on to their offspring. When the sperm and egg fuse, they form a zygote, or fertilized egg. The zygote has two sets of chromosomes—one set from the sperm and one set from the egg. Human eggs, for example, contain 23 total chromosomes in a set and sperm contain 23 total chromosomes in a set. So, each of your body cells contains one set of chromosomes from your mother and another set from your father for a total of 46 chromosomes.

Sex cells (sperm and egg) form through a process that reduces the chromosome number by half. It is through this process that homologous chromosomes separate into two different cells. This forms new cells with half as many chromosomes as the parent cell.

Homologous chromosomes have one chromosome from each parent. While the two chromosomes share the same sequence of genes, they may have different alleles. Before the chromosomes separate and move into separate cells, they undergo a process called crossing over. Notice in **Figure 5** that a small segment of one chromosome exchanges places with the corresponding segment on the other chromosome. By exchanging this genetic information, the new cells that form will have a slightly different combination of genes. This allows for minor variations in traits to form, which means there is a higher likelihood that offspring with desirable traits will form within the larger population.

Literacy Connection

Determine Meaning
Human body cells have twice as many chromosomes as sex cells. Underline statements that explain why body cells have two times as many chromosomes as sex cells.

Swapping Genetic Material

Figure 5 ✎ During crossing over, a segment of the gene from the mother changes places with a segment of the same gene from the father. Circle the gene segments that exchanged places.

CCC Cause and Effect
What would happen to offspring if crossing over did not occur?

....

....

....

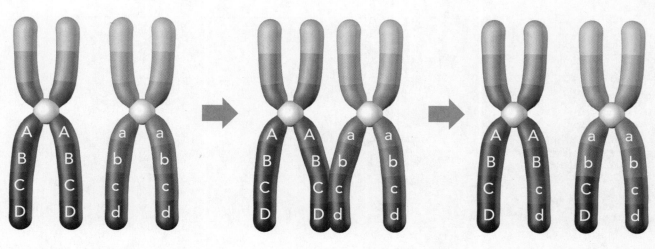

Homologous Chromosomes   **Crossing Over**   **Segments Exchange**

71

MS-LS3-1

Use the pedigree to answer questions 1 & 2.

In humans, free earlobes are dominant and attached earlobes are recessive. The pedigree shows the transmission of attached earlobes through four generations of a family.

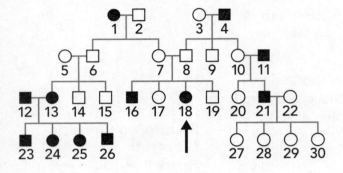

1. SEP Use Models Which male members of the family have attached earlobes?

....

....

2. Predict If the female marked by the arrow (individual 18) has a child with a male carrier, what is the probability their child will have attached earlobes?

....

....

3. SEP Provide Evidence Is chromosome number a good predictor of organism complexity? Explain.

....

....

....

....

....

....

4. SEP Use Mathematics A male king crab has 104 chromosomes in a sperm cell. How many chromosomes does it have in each of its body cells?

....

....

5. CCC Cause and Effect How can crossing over lead to the expression of new traits?

....

....

....

....

....

....

....

CAREERS
Genetic Counselor

Chromosome
COUNSELORS

Sometimes it runs in the family, as they say. We get traits such as eye color from genes passed on to us by our parents, but we can inherit diseases, too.

Genetic counselors help people who are at risk for a disease or a genetic disorder. They are experts in genetics, so they know better than anyone how genes work. And they are trained counselors, too. They give emotional support and help families make health decisions.

For example, a genetic counselor might help new parents of a baby with Down syndrome. Or the counselor might meet with a patient whose family has a history of Alzheimer's.

Genetic counselors study a family's health history, order genetic tests, and help people to live with a genetic disease. They even advise doctors. They're the genetic experts, and they share their knowledge to help people.

Genetic counselors complete a four-year bachelor's degree in biology or a healthcare field. After graduating, they work on completing a master's degree. This degree will focus on human genetics and counseling. They also complete extensive research. In addition, excellent communication and decision-making skills are required.

▶ VIDEO

Watch what's involved with being a genetic counselor.

📄 DOCUMENT

Go online to explore more science and engineering careers.

MY CAREER

Want to help people understand their genes? Do an online search for "genetic counselor" to learn more about this career.

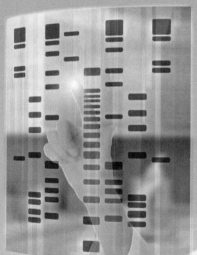

Phenomenon Genetic counselors help others understand the complex world of DNA, genes, and chromosomes.

73

(2) Trait Variations

MS-LS3-1 Develop and use a model to describe why structural changes to genes (mutations) located on chromosomes may affect proteins and may result in harmful, beneficial, or neutral effects to the structure and function of the organism.

MS-LS4-4 Construct an explanation based on evidence that describes how genetic variations of traits in a population increase some individuals' probability of surviving and reproducing in a specific environment. (Also **EP&CIIc**)

Connect It!

✎ **Circle a trait that distinguishes the male elephant seal from the female.**

Determine Differences What other differences do you notice between the male and female elephant seals?

....

....

CCC Structure and Function What traits allow the elephant seal to live in water? Explain your reasoning.

....

....

....

Diversity of Life

Organisms that are the same species tend to have many similarities. The Northern elephant seals in **Figure 1**, however, show that very different traits can exist in two individuals. Some differences are visible traits, such as wrinkled skin or brown hair. Others are invisible, such as type I diabetes or sickle-cell anemia in humans. Differences have the potential to be passed on from one generation to the next, and change the population.

The diversity of life on Earth relies in part on the variety of traits within a species. Any difference between individuals of the same species is a **variation**. Two friends with different eye color have a variation (green, brown) of the same trait (eye color). Variations may be due to DNA inherited from the parents, exposure to certain environmental factors, or a combination of both inheritance and environmental factors.

Variations can be helpful, harmful, or neutral. Consider a population of butterflies avoiding predators. Some have the same wing color pattern as a poisonous species. When this variation is passed from one generation to the next, the offspring are more likely to survive and reproduce. A harmful variation, on the other hand, threatens a population's survival. For example, low blood oxygen levels can be found in people with sickle-cell anemia. Neutral variations, such as different eye color, do not benefit or harm the population.

INTERACTIVITY

Identify traits found on a dog.

Northern Elephant Seals

Figure 1 These Northern elephant seals—two bellowing males and several females—relax on a beach near San Simeon. Although these seals are the same species and share most of the same DNA, there are differences in their appearances.

Chromosomes and Variation

You received 23 chromosomes from your mother and 23 chromosomes from your father. The combination of genes found on these chromosomes codes for the proteins that determine your traits.

Types of Chromosomes There are two types of chromosomes found in every one of your cells. Of the 23 pairs of chromosomes, one pair is sex chromosomes, while the other 22 pairs are autosomal chromosomes. **Sex chromosomes** are the pair of chromosomes carrying genes that determine whether a person is biologically male or female.

The combination of sex chromosomes determines the sex of the offspring. A human female inherits one X chromosome from her mother and one X chromosome from her father. A male receives one X chromosome from his mother and one Y chromosome from his father. **Figure 2** compares the X and Y chromosomes.

The 22 pairs of chromosomes that are not sex chromosomes are **autosomal chromosomes**. You inherit half of your autosomal chromosomes from your mother and half from your father. All the pairs of autosomal chromosomes are homologous chromosomes. This means that the genes for a trait are located at the same place on each chromosome in the pair, even though the alleles may be different. Females also have homologous sex chromosomes, while males do not.

INTERACTIVITY

Explore how some genetic disorders are carried on sex chromosomes.

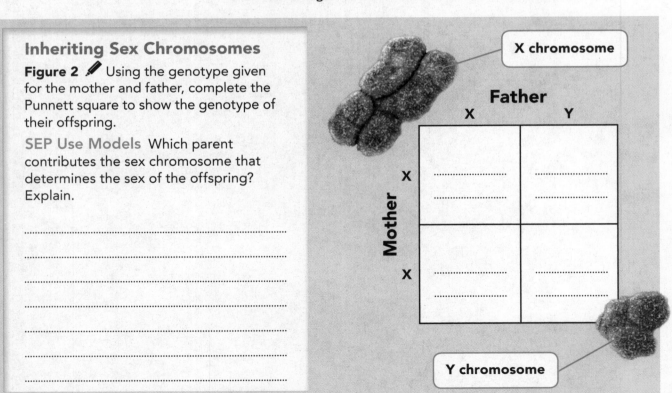

Inheriting Sex Chromosomes

Figure 2 ✏ Using the genotype given for the mother and father, complete the Punnett square to show the genotype of their offspring.

SEP Use Models Which parent contributes the sex chromosome that determines the sex of the offspring? Explain.

....

....

....

....

....

....

X chromosome

Father

X   Y

Mother   X

X

Y chromosome

Chromosome Size Chromosomes contain DNA, and each section of DNA that codes for a protein is a gene. DNA is made of small pieces called nitrogen bases. There are four different kinds of nitrogen bases, which always pair according to the same rules to form base pairs. For every trait, there is a gene or group of genes that controls the trait by producing proteins through the process of protein synthesis. Because the number of genes found on each chromosome and the length of each gene varies, chromosomes come in different sizes. For example, the X chromosome is almost three times the size of the Y chromosome and contains close to 16 times as many genes. Thus, it codes for more proteins, and determines more traits.

☑ CHECK POINT **Cite Textual Evidence** Why does the X chromosome express more traits than the Y chromosome?

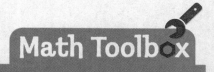

Math Toolbox

Chromosome and Gene Relationship

This data shows chromosome size as number of base pairs in the millions (Mbp) and estimated number of genes found on each one.

1. Construct a Scatter Plot ✏ Complete the scatter plot. Each dot represents the relationship between the total base pairs and the estimated number of genes for each chromosome.

Human Chromosome Size vs. Number of Genes

Estimated Number of Genes (y-axis: 0, 500, 1,000, 1,500, 2,000)

Millions of Base Pairs (Mbp) (x-axis: 0, 50, 100, 150, 200, 250)

2. SEP Interpret Data What relationship do you see between chromosome size and number of genes?

Chromosome	Mbp	Genes
1	248.96	2000
2	242.19	1300
3	198.3	1000
4	190.22	1000
5	181.54	900
6	170.81	1000
7	159.35	900
8	145.14	700
9	138.4	800
10	133.8	700
11	135.09	1300
12	133.28	1100
13	114.36	300
14	107.04	800
15	101.99	600
16	90.34	800
17	83.26	1200
18	80.37	200
19	58.62	1500
20	64.44	500
21	46.71	200
22	50.82	500
X	156.04	800
Y	57.23	50

Types of Mutations

An organism can develop traits due to changes in its genetic code. A **mutation** is any change in the DNA of a gene or chromosome. A mutation can cause an organism's trait to be different than what it normally would be. Mutations can be inherited from a parent or acquired during an organism's life. Inherited mutations occur when the parent passes on the mutation during reproduction. These mutations are present throughout the life of the organism, and are in every cell of the body. Acquired mutations occur at some point during an organism's lifetime. Acquired mutations can only be passed on from parent to offspring if the mutations occur in sex cells.

Genetic Mutations Many mutations are the result of small changes in the organism's DNA. Just one small change to an organism's genetic information is a mutation and may cause an incorrect protein to be made. As a result, the trait may be different from what was expressed before. **Figure 3** shows genetic mutations that can result when genetic information is deleted, added, or substituted.

Sex-Linked Mutations A mutation can occur on any chromosome. Some mutations occur on **sex-linked genes**, which are genes carried on a sex chromosome. Because the X chromosome has more genes than the Y chromosome, most sex-linked mutations occur on the X chromosome. In addition, many sex-linked mutations are recessive. Hemophilia is a recessive sex-linked mutation, where the individual's ability to clot blood is reduced. Males are more likely to exhibit hemophilia because they have only one X chromosome.

Genetic Mutations

Figure 3 The diagram shows three types of mutations.

Integrate with Visuals

✎ Find the three examples of mutation. Draw an arrow to show where a base pair was deleted. Circle where a base pair was added. Draw an X on the base pair that was substituted.

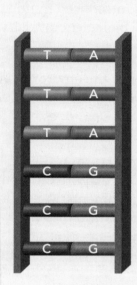

Original DNA sequence

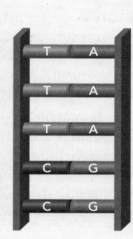

Deletion: one base pair is removed.

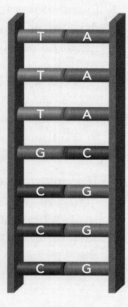

Addition: one base pair is added.

Substitution: one base pair is switched for another.

VIDEO

Investigate how mutations can affect organisms.

Environmental Factors

Interactions with our surroundings and the conditions in which we live have the potential to change the way genes are normally expressed. First, environmental factors can change an organism's genetic makeup. Secondly, the chemicals found on DNA can be changed.

Organisms encounter harmful chemicals and radiation on a regular basis. These agents are called mutagens because they can damage DNA in such way that it causes mutations. Some mutagens naturally occur, while others are synthetic. For example, radiation in the form of ultraviolet (UV) or X-rays are naturally occurring mutagens. Synthetic mutagens can be found in pesticides, asbestos, and food additives introduced by expanding human communities. Human introduced mutagens have the potential to negatively influence biological diversity.

Gene Expression Changes in the way genes are expressed may occur naturally or because of the environment. An example of natural change is when a caterpillar transitions to a butterfly. As the organism develops, the DNA does not change, but the genes are read and expressed differently.

The environment can change the way genes are expressed. Identical twins have the same DNA, but can acquire different traits when they grow up in different environments. Activities such as smoking and unhealthy eating habits can also alter the way genes are expressed, which changes a person's traits. **Figure 4** shows another way genes can be expressed differently.

Damage from Sun Exposure

Figure 4 🖊 UV radiation from the sun harms skin cells. UVA radiation penetrates into the deep layers of the skin and can alter skin structure. UVB radiation penetrates only the top layer of the skin. Draw arrows in the first diagram to show how deep UVA and UVB penetrate into the skin. Then, identify the radiation type—UVA or UVB—in the box next to the picture that shows a possible effect of the radiation.

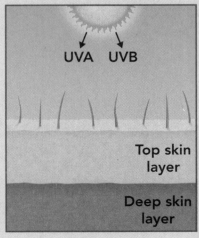

UVA   UVB

Top skin layer

Deep skin layer

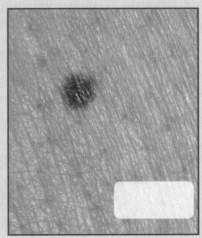

Camouflage
Figure 5 ✎ Sometimes mutations benefit the survival of a species. Predators will likely not see this animal, passing it as they swim. Circle the leopard flounder fish that is camouflaged.

Mutation Effects Mutations may be harmful, helpful, or neutral. Helpful mutations are those that benefit the survival of the species and are often passed on to offspring. Harmful mutations do not benefit the species and often decrease the likelihood of survival. Neutral mutations are those that do not affect an organism's chance of survival.

Helpful Mutations Some mutations can help an organism survive in their environment. One example of a helpful mutation is camouflage, which is the ability to blend in with the environment. In **Figure 5**, camouflage protects an organism from predators that may be looking for a meal. In humans, a mutation in a gene controlling fast-twitch muscles produces sprinters who are world-class athletes.

Harmful Mutations Genetic disorders and cancer are both the result of harmful mutations. A genetic disorder is an abnormal condition that a person inherits through genes or chromosomes. Cystic fibrosis is a genetic disorder that causes the body to make thick mucus in the lungs and digestive system. The mucus builds up in the lungs and blocks air flow. Cancer is a disease in which some body cells grow and divide uncontrollably, damaging the parts of the body around them. Few cancers are inherited. Most cancers are caused by acquired mutations that occur from damage to genes during the life of an organism.

Neutral Mutations Not all mutations are helpful or harmful. Some mutations, such as human hair color, may be neutral and have no impact on the survival of an organism. There may also be mutations that still code for the same protein. Even though the DNA sequence has changed, the amino acid that is produced remains the same.

☑ **CHECK POINT** **Distinguish Facts** In what ways can the environment impact the traits of an organism?

....

....

....

Mutations in Reproduction

Not all mutations are the result of small changes in the DNA in an organism's body cells. Some mutations occur when chromosomes do not separate correctly during the formation of sex cells. When this happens, a sex cell can end up with too many or too few chromosomes. When a chromosomal mutation occurs, either additional proteins are created or fewer proteins are created.

Protein Changes

Amino acids are the building blocks of proteins, which can be considered the architects of cell function. A change in the amino acid sequence can alter the final protein. The result is a mutation, which may or may not be detectable.

Some genes move to a new location on the genome. The movement could lead to a mutation due to changes in instructions to make the protein. Or, the instructions could remain intact, but now they are in a different place on the genome. Scientists are trying to understand the purpose of these 'jumping genes'. Sometimes they jump to a location that disrupts a functioning gene. When this occurs, the gene is not able to express itself, which can cause traits to change. Scientists speculate that jumping genes may cause a species to change. Scientists have also recently discovered that some species of octopus and squid, such as the one shown in **Figure 6**, are able to make specific proteins in response to a changing environment.

Changing RNA

Figure 6 Some organisms, such as this squid, can produce different proteins in response to a changing environment.

Synthesize Information Why is it beneficial for scientists to understand how other organisms are able to edit which proteins are created?

....

....

....

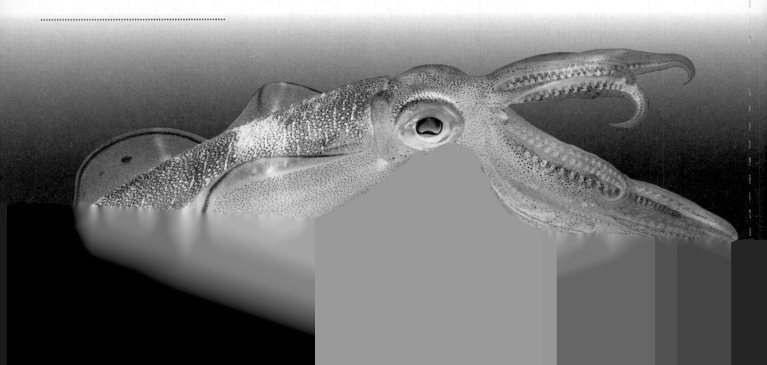

☑ LESSON 2 Check

MS-LS3-1, MS-LS4-4, EP&CIIc

1. SEP Communicate Information How can mutations change an organism's traits?

....

....

....

....

....

....

2. SEP Construct Explanations How is an organism's ability to produce offspring affected by changes to a chromosome?

....

....

....

....

....

....

3. Evaluate Claims A student states that only a male human offspring can express a recessive sex-linked X chromosome mutation. Is this statement accurate? Explain.

....

....

....

....

....

....

....

4. Connect to the Environment A scientist observes that members of a fish species near a popular beach had more acquired mutations than the same species in a river. Form a hypothesis stating how this difference could affect the future of the species.

....

....

....

....

....

....

....

5. SEP Construct an Argument If a baker making chocolate chip cookies accidentally misreads a recipe and adds something extra, forgets to add something, or adds the wrong ingredient, what can happen to the cookies? Explain how this analogy can be used to describe a mutation.

....

....

....

....

....

....

....

....

....

83

Genetic Technologies

HANDS-ON LAB

uInvestigate Extract DNA from a strawberry.

MS-LS4-5 Gather and synthesize information about the technologies that have changed the way humans influence the inheritance of desired traits in organisms.

Connect It!

✏️ **Dogs come in many different shapes, sizes, and colors. Which of the ones shown here would you prefer as a pet? Circle your choice.**

CCC Cause and Effect Many purebred dogs have problems later in life, such as joint or eye diseases. Why are purebred dogs more likely to develop problems later in life?

....

....

Make Inferences What can be done to decrease the likelihood of these problems appearing?

....

....

Artificial Selection

When consumers make choices, they are often attracted to products with the highest quality. We want the healthiest and best-tasting fruits and vegetables. We want the right amount of fat and flavor in our meats. We even want the best traits in our pets, such as the dogs you see in **Figure 1**. These high-quality products do not appear only in nature. Scientists and breeders have influenced the traits that other organisms inherit through the process of selective breeding.

Selective Breeding In the natural world, individuals with beneficial traits are more likely to survive and successfully reproduce than individuals without those traits. This is called natural selection. **Artificial selection** is also known as selective breeding. It occurs when humans breed only those organisms with desired traits to produce the next generation. It's important to note that desired traits are not necessarily the traits that benefit the organism's chances for survival. Instead, they are traits that humans desire.

Dogs, cats, and livestock animals have all been selectively bred. Cows, chickens, and pigs have been bred to be larger so that they produce more milk or meat. Breeding and caring for farm animals that have certain genetic traits that humans desire is called animal husbandry. The many different breeds of dogs shown in **Figure 1** have also been bred over time for very specific functions.

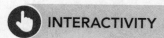
INTERACTIVITY

Take a poll about genetic modification in food.

Literacy Connection

Corroborate Find statements in the text that support the claim that artificial selection is not a natural process and does not necessarily help the organism's survival.

Purebred Dogs
Figure 1 Each type of purebred dog shown here is the result of selective breeding over the course of many generations.

Genetic Engineering

With the discovery of DNA and its relationship to genes, scientists have developed more methods to produce desired traits. Through a process called **genetic engineering**, modern geneticists can transfer a gene from the DNA of one organism into another. Genetic engineering is used to give organisms genes they could not acquire through breeding.

Scientists use genetic engineering techniques to insert specific desired genes into animals. By **manipulating** a gene, scientists have created a fish that glows when under a black light **(Figure 2)**. A jellyfish gene for fluorescence was inserted into a fertilized fish egg to produce the glowing fish. Scientists are hoping that further research on this gene will lead to a method that helps track toxic chemicals in the body.

Genetic engineering is also used to synthesize materials. A protein hormone called insulin helps control blood-sugar levels after eating. People who have diabetes cannot effectively control their blood-sugar levels, and many must take insulin injections. Prior to 1980, some diabetics were injecting themselves with insulin from other animals without getting the desired results. To help diabetics, scientists genetically engineered bacteria to produce the first human protein—insulin. The process they used, and still use today, is shown in **Figure 3**. Furthermore, bacteria can reproduce quickly, so large amounts of human insulin are produced in a short time.

Glowing Fish
Figure 2 Genetic engineering made glowing fish possible.

Academic Vocabulary
Explain the difference between manipulating a tool and manipulating another person.

....

....

....

....

....

....

Plan It

Synthesize a New Trait
✎ Create a trait that has never been seen before in an animal. Identify a trait you would like an animal to have. Then, sketch the animal and describe a process by which you could achieve your desired result.

....

....

....

....

....

....

....

Bacteria Make Human Insulin

Figure 3 ✏ Bacteria can be used to produce insulin in humans. Complete the diagram by showing the process for Step 5.

HANDS-ON LAB

и**Investigate** Extract DNA from a strawberry.

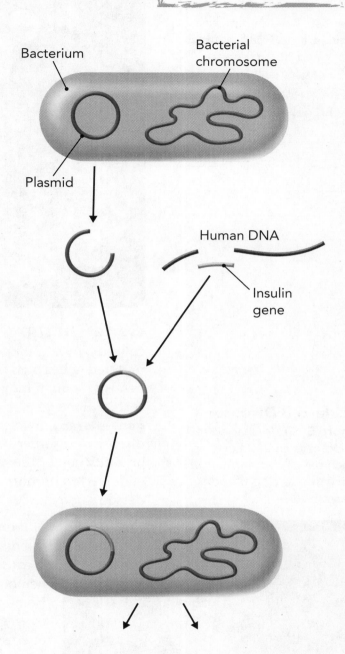

❶ Small rings of DNA, or plasmids, are found in some bacteria cells.

❷ Scientists remove the plasmid and cut it open with an enzyme. They then insert an insulin gene that has been removed from human DNA.

❸ The human insulin gene attaches to the open ends of the plasmid to form a closed ring.

❹ Some bacteria cells take up the plasmids that have the insulin gene.

❺ When the cells reproduce, the new cells contain copies of the "engineered" plasmid. The foreign gene directs the cells to produce human insulin.

T-cell Destroys Cancer Cell

Figure 4 T-cells are a type of white blood cell that help to fight disease in your body. Scientists have genetically engineered a T-cell that can attack and destroy up to 1,000 cancer cells.

Predict How might doctors use this new T-cell?

....

....

....

....

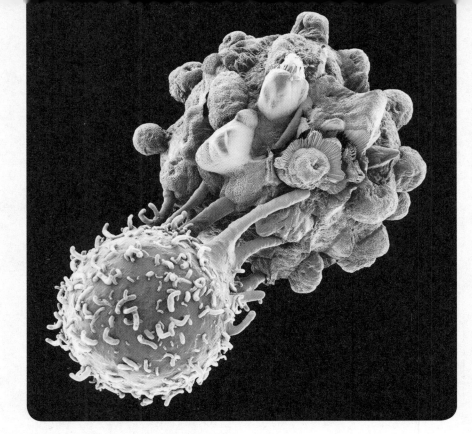

Sickle-cell Disease

Figure 5 Sickle-shaped red blood cells cannot carry as much oxygen as normal cells and can also clog blood vessels.

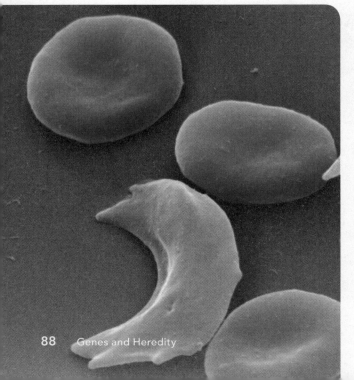

Gene Therapy in Humans Genetic diseases are caused by mutations, or changes in the DNA code. Some mutated genes pass from parent to child; others occur spontaneously. Soon, it may be possible to use genetic engineering to correct some genetic disorders in humans. This process, called **gene therapy**, involves changing a gene to treat a medical disease or disorder. A normal working gene replaces an absent or faulty gene. One promising therapy involves genetically engineering immune-system cells and injecting them into a person's body.

Millions of people worldwide suffer from sickle cell disease. This painful genetic disorder is caused by a single mutation that affects hemoglobin, a protein in red blood cells. Hemoglobin carries oxygen. The mutation causes the blood cells to be shaped like a sickle, or crescent, as shown in **Figure 5.**

CRISPR is a gene-editing tool that can potentially help people with sickle cell disease. CRISPR uses a "guide RNA" and an enzyme to cut out the DNA sequence causing the dangerous mutation. The "guide RNA" takes the enzyme to the DNA sequence with the sickle cell mutation, and the enzyme then removes that sequence. Then another tool pastes a copy of the normal sequence into the DNA.

Cloning Organisms

A **clone** is an organism that has the same genes as the organism from which it was produced. The process of cloning involves removing an unfertilized egg and replacing its nucleus with the nucleus of a body cell from the same species. Because this body cell has a full set of chromosomes, the offspring will have the same DNA as the individual that donated the body cell. The egg is then implanted into a female so it can develop. If the process is successful, the clone is born.

Cloning is used to develop many of the foods we eat. Many plants are cloned simply by taking a small piece of the original and putting it in suitable conditions to grow. For example, the Cavendish banana (see **Figure 6**) is the most common banana for eating. All these bananas are clones of the original plant. Cloning helps to produce crops of consistent quality. But a population with little genetic diversity has drawbacks, both for farmers and for people who rely on the crop for food.

✓ **CHECK POINT** **Summarize Text** List the steps in creating a clone.

....

....

....

....

▶ **VIDEO**

Learn how selective breeding and cloning can lead to populations with desired traits.

Write About It
Cloning food crops has many advantages. Every commercial banana crop, worldwide, is cloned. Write about how a disease that destroyed the Cavendish banana could affect society. Consider farmers, fruit companies, grocery stores, everyday people, and others who would be affected.

Cloned Bananas
Figure 6 A fungus that causes bananas to rot is spreading across the globe. The Cavendish banana is particularly vulnerable.

SEP Construct Explanations
Why is a disease more damaging to cloned crops?

....

....

....

....

....

....

Practical Uses for DNA

Due to new technologies, geneticists now study and use genes in ways that weren't possible before. Modern geneticists can now determine the exact sequence of nitrogen bases in an organism's DNA. This process is called DNA sequencing.

Sequencing the Human Genome Breaking a code with six billion letters may seem like an impossible task to undertake. But scientists working on the Human Genome Project did just that. The complete set of genetic information that an organism carries in its DNA is called a **genome**. The main goal of the Human Genome Project was to identify the DNA sequence of the entire human genome. Since sequencing the human genome, scientists now research the functions of tens of thousands of human genes. Some of these genes also allow scientists to better understand certain diseases.

Our genome can also help us understand how humans evolved on Earth. All life on Earth evolved from simple, single-celled organisms that lived billions of years ago, and we still have evidence of this in our DNA. For example, there are some genes that exist in the cells of almost every organism on Earth, which suggests we all evolved from a common ancestor. Some organisms share a closer relationship than others. By comparing genomes of organisms, scientists continue to piece together a history of how life on Earth evolved.

DNA Technologies Before the Human Genome Project, scientists such as Gregor Mendel used experimentation to understand heredity. Since the project's completion in 2003, the use of technologies to understand heredity and how DNA guides life processes has increased greatly. For example, DNA technologies help diagnose genetic diseases.

Genetic disorders typically result from one or more changed genes, called mutations. Medical specialists can carry out a DNA screening to detect the presence of a mutation. To complete a DNA screen, samples of DNA are analyzed for the presence of one or more mutated genes. This information is then used to help those individuals whose DNA includes mutated genes.

DNA comparisons determine how closely related you are to another person. To do this, DNA from a person's cell is broken down into small pieces, or fragments. These fragments are put into a machine that separates them by size. When this happens, a pattern is produced creating a DNA fingerprint, like the one shown in **Figure 8**. Similarities between patterns determine who contributed the DNA. Genetic fingerprints can be used to tie a person to a crime scene, prevent the wrong person from going to jail, identify remains, or identify the father of a child.

INTERACTIVITY

Consider using technology to solve the world's food problem.

DNA Fingerprint

Figure 8 ✏ Circle the suspect that left his or her DNA at the crime scene.

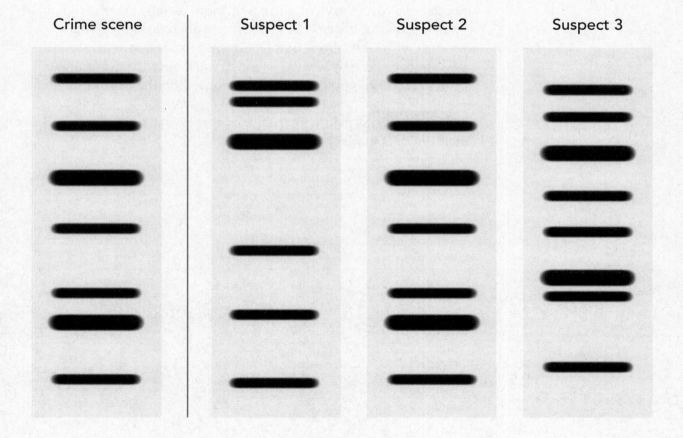

| Crime scene | Suspect 1 | Suspect 2 | Suspect 3 |

Controversies of DNA Use

As genetic research advances, some people are concerned about how genetic information will be used or altered. Some people are concerned about who can access their DNA information and how this information will be used.

Your genetic information is the only truly unique part of your identity, and many people want to keep it as private as possible. The Genetic Information Nondiscrimination Act (GINA) was signed into law in 2008. This act makes it illegal for health insurance companies and employers to discriminate against individuals based on genetic information. Health insurance companies cannot deny you care, and a company cannot refuse to hire you simply because of the results of a genetic test (**Figure 9**). Your genetic information cannot be used without your consent, and it must be used in a way that is fair and just.

Some people are concerned about the use of genetically modified organisms (GMOs) in the food supply. GMOs are made by changing DNA so desired traits are expressed. Growing our food from seeds that have been genetically modified is controversial. Many people fear the impact it could have on human health and the environment in the future. One concern is that DNA from GMOs could mix with DNA from wild organisms when they reproduce. This might introduce traits into a population that are not beneficial for survival, since GMOs are usually engineered to grow faster or taste better. Yet farmers are able to yield more product with GMO crops that engineered to not be eaten by pests or overcome by weeds. Scientists must balance sustaining a growing human population with safeguarding the environment.

✓ CHECK POINT **Cite Textual Evidence** What are the pros and cons of GMO foods?

....

....

....

....

....

....

....

....

....

Using Genetic Information

Figure 9 Some people fear that medical insurance companies will not cover their medical expenses if they have been genetically tested and results show a genetic disorder.

Evaluate Reasoning Why is this a fear of many people? What can we do to protect our privacy?

....

....

....

....

....

....

....

....

....

....

MS-LS4-5

1. Identify Shortly after World War II, chickens were bred to grow much more quickly and to produce much more meat. Which process is this an example of?

....

2. Compare and Contrast What are some positive and negative ways that genetic information may be used?

....

....

....

3. CCC Cause and Effect Some genetically engineered organisms can mate with wild members of their species. Farmed fish are often genetically modified. What can happen to wild fish of their species if mating occurs?

....

....

....

4. SEP Construct Explanations Gorillas and humans evolved from a common ancestor. Geneticists found that they may be more closely related than previously thought. How can DNA sequencing of the gorilla and human genomes determine this?

....

....

....

5. SEP Evaluate Information A classmate states that animals that result from artificial selection are "lucky," since they have better traits than naturally bred animals. Given your study of this topic, do you agree? Explain.

....

....

....

....

6. CCC Relate Structure and Function How can changes to the structure of DNA lead to the development of new traits in a species?

....

....

....

....

....

....

....

....

....

....

7. SEP Design Solutions The procedure used to make insulin in bacteria can also be used to synthesize other biological materials. Think of a chemical or material inside the human body that might be synthesized within bacteria. What would be the potential benefits of this process? What would be the potential drawbacks?

....

....

....

....

....

....

....

....

....

....

....

....

littleBits™

MS-LS4-5

REINVENTING DNA AS
Data Storage

 VIDEO

Discover how scientists use DNA to solve data storage problems.

How much digital space do you need for all your texts, emails, photos, and music? Digital information can take up lots of space.

Code	P	l	a	y
Binary data	01010000	01101100	01100001	01111001
DNA nucleotides	GCGAG	ATCGA	AGAGC	TGCTCT

The Challenge: To provide storage solutions for the data storage needs of everyone on Earth.

Phenomenon Some estimates state that the world has 40 trillion gigabytes (GB) of data. Forty trillion GB equals about 40 million petabytes (PB). Ten billion photos on social media sites use about 1.5 PB. So, if every star in our Milky Way galaxy were one byte of data, then we would need 5,000 Milky Ways, each with 200 billion stars, to amass one PB of data. How can we possibly store all of our data?

Science may offer an answer: DNA. Our entire genetic code fits within the nucleus of a single cell. Scientists have figured out how to convert digital data (in 1s and 0s) into DNA's A-C-T-G code. Then they constructed synthetic DNA in a lab. So far, scientists have been able to encode and store images and videos within a single strand of DNA. If current cost constraints are overcome, DNA could be the next microchip. Someday, the data currently stored on computers in enormous buildings may fit in the palm of your hand!

Science may solve the engineering problem of our exploding data storage needs. Scientists can store documents and photos by converting digital code to DNA code and then making synthetic DNA. To retrieve a file, the DNA code gets converted back to digital code.

 **DESIGN CHALLENGE** Can you design your own code to store information? Go to the Engineering Design Notebook to find out!

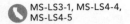
MS-LS3-1, MS-LS4-4, MS-LS4-5

Evidence-Based Assessment

Scientists have figured out a way to insert the genes of one organism into another. A genetically modified organism, GMO, expresses, or shows, desired traits that prove to be beneficial to many farmers. Reliance on GMO crops has been increasing in the United States for many years.

The graph shows three genetically modified crops—corn, soybeans, and cotton. In each crop, the DNA has been engineered for a desired trait. New DNA sequences that code for specific proteins are inserted into a crop's DNA.

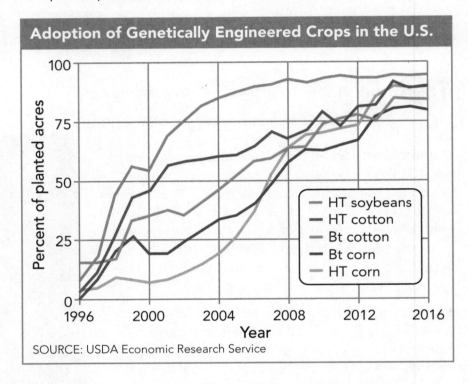

Adoption of Genetically Engineered Crops in the U.S.

- — HT soybeans
- — HT cotton
- — Bt cotton
- — Bt corn
- — HT corn

SOURCE: USDA Economic Research Service

For example, some crops have been engineered to resist droughts. The gene for drought resistance is cut from the DNA of a desert-dwelling species and then inserted into the crop species. The resistance-to-drought trait will be expressed when these genetically engineered crop plants reproduce. In the graph, you can observe data on another desirable trait that has been produced through genetic engineering is improved herbicide tolerance (HT). This trait protects the GMO crop when herbicides are sprayed on the fields to kill weeds. The Bt crop includes a gene from the *Bacillus thuringiensis* bacterium. This gene produces a protein that kills the larvae of the corn borer, a pest. Farmers can grow Bt crops instead of spraying insecticides that could also kill helpful insects, such as bees.

1. **SEP Analyze Data** Which genetically engineered crop has shown the greatest increase in usage from 2006 to 2016?

   A. HT Corn   **B.** Bt Corn

   C. HT Cotton   **D.** HT Soybeans

2. **CCC Patterns** What patterns do you observe in the line graphs for the crops that are herbicide tolerant, HT? Support your claim.

   ....

   ....

   ....

   ....

   ....

   ....

   ....

   ....

   ....

   ....

   ....

   ....

   ....

   ....

   ....

   ....

3. **Connect to the Environment** Which statement is true about GMO crops?

   ☐ GMOs reduce the need for chemical pesticides.

   ☐ Years of research confirm that GMOs are safe for human consumption.

   ☐ GMOs increase the need for chemical pesticides.

4. **CCC Stability and Change** Each box below contains an idea about why genetically engineered crops may be used in the future. Sequence the boxes to infer how the ideas would be used in a flowchart.

   | GMO crops now account for most acres of farm land. | _____ |

   | Use of GMOs has been increasing for ten years. | _____ |

   | This trend will continue because it saves time and money. | _____ |

MS-LS3-1

Modeling Mutations

How can you use a **model** to show how **mutations** work?

Background

Phenomenon You have observed the phenomenon of mutations whether you have realized it or not. A fruit or vegetable in a grocery store that is not quite the right color or shape, or an animal that has discolored fur, hair, or skin might be expressing genetic mutations.

We can use models to show what a mutation is. Small mutations in genes can result in changes to proteins. These changes can affect the structures and functions of the organism. Mutations can have a positive, negative, or neutral effect on an organism.

Materials

Paper and pencil

Design Your Investigation

1. Think of a short word.
2. Write the word here.

....

Procedure

HANDS-ON LAB

uDemonstrate Go online for a downloadable worksheet for this lab.

3. Write a code for a mutation.
4. Write 3 new codes for 3 more mutations from the previous mutation.
5. Diagram your word model below and identify what the mutation was.

Develop Your Model

Analyze and Interpret Data

1. **SEP Develop a Model** How did each mutation affect your word?

....
....
....
....
....

2. **SEP Analyze Data** How would you categorize the changes?

....
....
....
....
....

3. **SEP Use a Model to Evaluate** How does your model represent a mutation?

....
....
....
....
....

4. **CCC Cause and Effect** How can mutations affect organisms? Provide an example.

....
....
....
....
....

Take Notes

Use this space for recording notes and sketching out ideas.

Revisit the Anchoring Phenomenon
Conduct an Investigation

Evidence **Now that you have completed the two topics in this segment, do the following tasks.**

Make Generalizations The Sacramento River is the longest in California. It draws from many watersheds. The first map shows current habitat for spring-run Chinook salmon. Outside this zone, river water conditions cannot support healthy populations or the rivers are not accessible by the fish. The second map shows the locations of dams across the state.

There are more than 1,400 dams across the state.

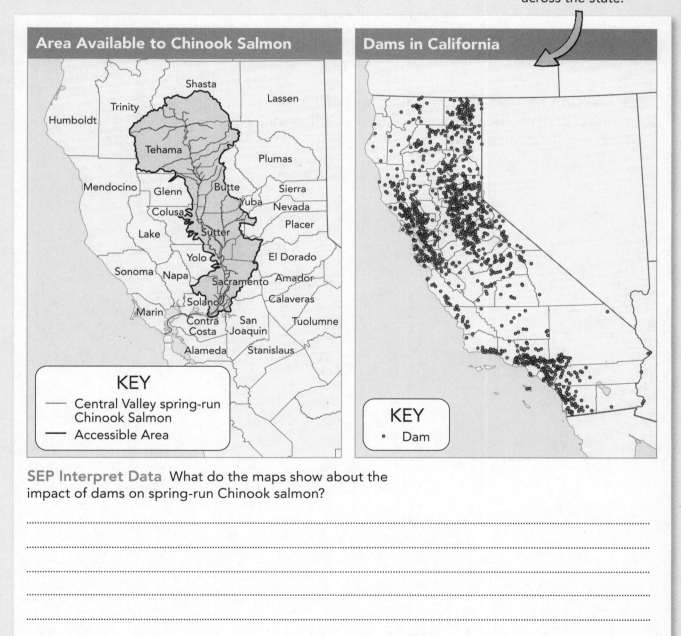

Area Available to Chinook Salmon

KEY
— Central Valley spring-run Chinook Salmon
— Accessible Area

Dams in California

KEY
• Dam

SEP Interpret Data What do the maps show about the impact of dams on spring-run Chinook salmon?

....

....

....

....

....

....

Design a Solution

Team up with a small group of classmates. Together, list the issues facing native fish species in California today. Talk about the factors that affect their growth and reproduction. Which factors have the greatest impact on the health of the species? Are the factors environmental, genetic, or a combination of both?

Make a plan to help an endangered native California fish species.

1. Go to this website to see a list of fish species in California: http://calfish.ucdavis.edu/species/

2. Find a native species.

3. Click on the name of the fish to read about its life history.

SEP Develop Models ✏ In the space provided, sketch and describe your plan. Then, explain how your solution will help the fish population to survive.

....

....

....

....

....

Communicate a Solution

Based on your analysis of the data and your research, answer the following questions.

1. **SEP Communicate Information** Which fish species did you choose? Briefly describe any inherited traits of fish, their habitat, and any behaviors that help them to reproduce.

_____

_____

_____

_____

_____

2. **CCC Cause and Effect** How might climate change and low genetic diversity impact your fish species?

_____

_____

_____

_____

3. **SEP Engage in Argument** During long droughts, fresh water is very precious. Farmers need the water for their crops. People need fresh drinking water. Do you think it's important to provide water to fish during droughts by releasing dam water? Explain.

_____

_____

_____

_____

4. **SEP Design a Solution** Some of the ways that humans use natural resources have long-term consequences. Consider some of the reasons humans build dams. One is to generate electricity. Another is to provide fresh drinking water. Some people suggest removing dams to help restore ecosystems. What could people do instead to get the fresh water they need in a way that limits these consequences?

_____

_____

_____

Safety Symbols

These symbols warn of possible dangers in the laboratory and remind you to work carefully.

 Safety Goggles Wear safety goggles to protect your eyes in any activity involving chemicals, flames or heating, or glassware.

 Lab Apron Wear a laboratory apron to protect your skin and clothing from damage.

 Breakage Handle breakable materials, such as glassware, with care. Do not touch broken glassware.

 Heat-Resistant Gloves Use an oven mitt or other hand protection when handling hot materials, such as hot plates or hot glassware.

 Plastic Gloves Wear disposable plastic gloves when working with harmful chemicals and organisms. Keep your hands away from your face, and dispose of the gloves according to your teacher's instructions.

 Heating Use a clamp or tongs to pick up hot glassware. Do not touch hot objects with your bare hands.

 Flames Before you work with flames, tie back loose hair and clothing. Follow your teacher's instructions about lighting and extinguishing flames.

 No Flames When using flammable materials, make sure there are no flames, sparks, or other exposed heat sources present.

 Corrosive Chemical Avoid getting acid or other corrosive chemicals on your skin or clothing or in your eyes. Do not inhale the vapors. Wash your hands after the activity.

 Poison Do not let any poisonous chemical come into contact with your skin, and do not inhale its vapors. Wash your hands when you are finished with the activity.

 Fumes Work in a well-ventilated area when harmful vapors may be involved. Avoid inhaling vapors directly. Test an odor only when directed to do so by your teacher, and use a wafting motion to direct the vapor toward your nose.

 Sharp Object Scissors, scalpels, knives, needles, pins, and tacks can cut your skin. Always direct a sharp edge or point away from yourself and others.

 Animal Safety Treat live or preserved animals or animal parts with care to avoid harming the animals or yourself. Wash your hands when you are finished with the activity.

 Plant Safety Handle plants only as directed by your teacher. If you are allergic to certain plants, tell your teacher; do not do an activity involving those plants. Avoid touching harmful plants such as poison ivy. Wash your hands when you are finished with the activity.

 Electric Shock To avoid electric shock, never use electrical equipment around water, when the equipment is wet, or when your hands are wet. Be sure cords are untangled and cannot trip anyone. Unplug equipment not in use.

 Physical Safety When an experiment involves physical activity, avoid injuring yourself or others. Alert your teacher if there is any reason you should not participate.

 Disposal Dispose of chemicals and other laboratory materials safely. Follow the instructions from your teacher.

 Hand Washing Wash your hands thoroughly when finished with an activity. Use soap and warm water. Rinse well.

 General Safety Awareness When this symbol appears, follow the instructions provided. When you are asked to develop your own procedure in a lab, have your teacher approve your plan.

GLOSSARY

abiotic factor A nonliving part of an organism's habitat.

adaptation An inherited behavior or physical characteristic that helps an organism survive and reproduce in its environment.

allele A different form of a gene.

alveoli Tiny sacs of lung tissue specialized for the movement of gases between air and blood.

artery A blood vessel that carries blood away from the heart.

artificial selection The process by which humans breed only those organisms with desired traits to produce the next generation; selective breeding.

asexual reproduction A reproductive process that involves only one parent and produces offspring that are genetically identical to the parent.

autosomal chromosomes The 22 pairs of chromosomes that are not sex chromosomes.

autotroph An organism that is able to capture energy from sunlight or chemicals and use it to produce its own food.

auxin A hormone that controls a plant's growth and response to light.

bacteria Single-celled organisms that lack a nucleus; prokaryotes.

behavior The way an organism reacts to changes in its internal conditions or external environment.

biodiversity The number and variety of different species in an area.

biotic factor A living or once living part of an organism's habitat.

brain The part of the central nervous system that is located in the skull and controls most functions in the body.

bronchi The passages that direct air into the lungs.

capillary A tiny blood vessel where substances are exchanged between the blood and the body cells.

carbohydrate An energy-rich organic compound, such as a sugar or a starch, that is made of the elements of carbon, hydrogen, and oxygen.

cell The basic unit of structure and function in living things.

cell membrane A thin, flexible barrier that surrounds a cell and controls which substances pass into and out of a cell.

cell wall A rigid supporting layer that surrounds the cells of plants and some other organisms.

cellular respiration The process in which oxygen and glucose undergo a complex series of chemical reactions inside cells, releasing energy.

chlorophyll A green photosynthetic pigment found in the chloroplasts of plants, algae, and some bacteria.

chloroplast An organelle in the cells of plants and some other organisms that captures energy from sunlight and changes it to an energy form that cells can use in making food.

chromosome A threadlike structure within a cell's nucleus that contains DNA that is passed from one generation to the next.

circulatory system An organ system that taransports needed materials to cells and removes wastes.

clone An organism that is genetically identical to the organism from which it was produced.

commensalism A type of symbiosis between two species in which one species benefits and the other species is neither helped nor harmed.

community All the different populations that live together in a certain area.

competition The struggle between organisms to survive as they attempt to use the same limited resources in the same place at the same time.

condensation The change in state from a gas to a liquid.

cones The reproductive structures of gymnosperms.

conservation The practice of using less of a resource so that it can last longer.

consumer An organism that obtains energy by feeding on other organisms.

cytoplasm The thick fluid region of a cell located inside the cell membrane (in prokaryotes) or between the cell membrane and nucleus (in eukaryotes).

D

decomposer An organism that gets energy by breaking down biotic wastes and dead organisms and returns raw materials to the soil and water.

diffusion The process by which molecules move from an area of higher concentration to an area of lower concentration.

digestion The process that breaks complex molecules of food into smaller nutrient molecules.

dominant allele An allele whose trait always shows up in the organism when the allele is present.

dormancy A period of time when an organism's growth or activity stops.

E

ecological restoration The practice of helping a degraded or destroyed ecosystem recover from damage.

ecology The study of how organisms interact with each other and their environment.

ecosystem The community of organisms that live in a particular area, along with their nonliving environment.

ecosystem services The benefits that humans derive from ecosystems.

embryo The young organism that develops from a zygote.

endocytosis The process by which the cell membrane takes particles into the cell by changing shape and engulfing the particles.

energy pyramid A diagram that shows the amount of energy that moves from one feeding level to another in a food web.

enzyme A type of protein that speeds up chemical reactions in the body.

evaporation The process by which molecules at the surface of a liquid absorb enough energy to change to a gas.

evolution Change over time; the process by which modern organisms have descended from ancient organisms.

excretion The process by which wastes are removed from the body.

exocytosis The process by which the vacuole surrounding particles fuses with the cell membrane, forcing the contents out of the cell.

extinct Term used to refer to a group of related organisms that has died out and has no living members.

extinction The disappearance of all members of a species from Earth.

F

fermentation The process by which cells release energy by breaking down food molecules without using oxygen.

fertilization The process in sexual reproduction in which an egg cell and a sperm cell join to form a new cell.

fitness How well an organism can survive and reproduce in its environment.

food chain A series of events in an ecosystem in which organisms transfer energy by eating and by being eaten.

food web The pattern of overlapping feeding relationships or food chains among the various organisms in an ecosystem.

fossil The preserved remains or traces of an organism that lived in the past.

fossil record All the fossils that have been discovered and what scientists have learned from them.

fragmentation A type of asexual reproduction in which a new organism forms from a piece of a parent organism.

fruit The ripened ovary and other structures of an angiosperm that enclose one or more seeds.

G

gene A sequence of DNA that determines a trait and is passed from parent to offspring.

gene therapy The process of replacing an absent or faulty gene with a normal working gene to treat a disease or medical disorder.

genetic engineering The transfer of a gene from the DNA of one organism into another organism, in order to produce an organism with desired traits.

GLOSSARY

genome The complete set of genetic information that an organism carries in its DNA.

germination The sprouting of the embryo out of a seed; occurs when the embryo resumes its growth following dormancy.

gland An organ that produces and releases chemicals either through ducts or into the bloodstream.

H

habitat An environment that provides the things a specific organism needs to live, grow, and reproduce.

heredity The passing of traits from parents to offspring.

heterotroph An organism that cannot make its own food and gets food by consuming other living things.

homeostasis The condition in which an organism's internal environment is kept stable in spite of changes in the external environment.

homologous structures Structures that are similar in different species and that have been inherited from a common ancestor.

hormone The chemical produced by an endocrine gland.; A chemical that affects growth and development.

host An organism that provides a source of energy or a suitable environment for a parasite to live with, in, or on.

I

inheritance The process by which an offspring receives genes from its parents.

instinct A response to a stimulus that is inborn.

invasive species Species that are not native to a habitat and can out-compete native species in an ecosystem.

invertebrate An animal without a backbone.

K

keystone species A species that influences the survival of many other species in an ecosystem.

L

limiting factor An environmental factor that causes a population to decrease in size.

lymph Fluid that travels through the lymphatic system consisting of water, white blood cells, and dissolved materials.

M

mammal A vertebrate whose body temperature is regulated by its internal heat, and that has skin covered with hair or fur and glands that produce milk to feed its young.

mating system Behavior patterns related to how animals mate.

mechanism The natural process by which something takes place.

migration The regular, seasonal journey of an animal from one place to another and back again.

mitochondria Rod-shaped organelles that convert energy in food molecules to energy the cell can use to carry out its functions.

molecule A group of small, nonliving particles that make up all material.

multicellular Consisting of many cells.

mutation Any change in the DNA of a gene or a chromosome.

mutualism A type of symbiosis in which both species benefit from living together.

N

natural resource Anything naturally occurring in the environment that humans use.

natural selection The process by which organisms that are best adapted to their environment are most likely to survive and reproduce.

negative feedback A process in which a system is turned off by the condition it produces.

nephron Small filtering structure found in the kidneys that removes wastes from blood and produces urine.

neuron A cell that carries information through the nervous system.

nucleus In cells, a large oval organelle that contains the cell's genetic material in the form of DNA and controls many of the cell's activities.

nutrients Substances in food that provide the raw materials and energy needed for an organism to carry out its essential processes.

O
---

organ A body structure that is composed of different kinds of tissues that work together.

organ system A group of organs that work together to perform a major function.

organelle A tiny cell structure that carries out a specific function within the cell.

organism A living thing.

osmosis The diffusion of water molecules across a selectively permeable membrane.

ovule A plant structure in seed plants that produces the female gametophyte; contains an egg cell.

P
---

parasite An organism that benefits by living with, on, or in a host in a parasitism interaction.

parasitism A type of symbiosis in which one organism lives with, on, or in a host and harms it.

peristalsis Waves of smooth muscle contractions that move food through the esophagus toward the stomach.

pheromone A chemical released by one animal that affects the behavior of another animal of the same species.

photoperiodism A plant's response to seasonal changes in the length of night and day.

photosynthesis The process by which plants and other autotrophs capture and use light energy to make food from carbon dioxide and water.

pioneer species The first species to populate an area during succession.

pollination The transfer of pollen from male reproductive structures to female reproductive structures in plants.

population All the members of one species living in the same area.

precipitation Any form of water that falls from clouds and reaches Earth's surface as rain, snow, sleet, or hail.

predation An interaction in which one organism kills another for food or nutrients.

probability A number that describes how likely it is that a particular event will occur.

producer An organism that can make its own food.

protein Large organic molecule made of carbon, hydrogen, oxygen, nitrogen, and sometimes sulfur.

protist A eukaryotic organism that cannot be classified as an animal, plant, or fungus.

R
---

recessive allele An allele that is hidden whenever the dominant allele is present.

reflex An automatic response that occurs rapidly and without conscious control.

response An action or change in behavior that occurs as a result of a stimulus.

S
---

saliva A fluid produced in the mouth that aids in mechanical and chemical digestion.

scientific theory A well-tested explanation for a wide range of observations or experimental results.

selectively permeable A property of cell membranes that allows some substances to pass across it, while others cannot.

sex chromosomes The pair of chromosomes carrying genes that determine whether a person is biologically male or female.

sex-linked gene A gene carried on a sex chromosome.

sexual reproduction A reproductive process that involves two parents that combine their genetic material to produce a new organism which differs from both parents.

species A group of similar organisms that can mate with each other and produce offspring that can also mate and reproduce.

GLOSSARY

spinal cord A thick column of nervous tissue that links the brain to nerves in the body.

spontaneous generation The mistaken idea that living things arise from nonliving sources.

stimulus Any change or signal in the environment that can make an organism react in some way.

stress The reaction of a person's body to potentially threatening, challenging, or disturbing events.

succession The series of predictable changes that occur in a community over time.

sustainability The ability of an ecosystem to maintain bioviersity and production indefinitely.

symbiosis Any relationship in which two species live closely together and that benefits at least one of the species.

synapse The junction where one neuron can transfer an impulse to the next structure.

_____ **T** _____

tissue A group of similar cells that perform a specific function.

trait A specific characteristic that an organism can pass to its offspring through its genes.

tropism A plant's growth response toward or away from a stimulus.

_____ **U** _____

unicellular Made of a single cell.

_____ **V** _____

vaccine A substance used in a vaccination that consists of pathogens that have been weakened or killed but can still trigger the body to produce chemicals that destroy the pathogens.

vacuole A sac-like organelle that stores water, food, and other materials.

variation Any difference between individuals of the same species.

vein A blood vessel that carries blood back to the heart.

vertebrate An animal with a backbone.

virus A tiny, nonliving particle that enters and then reproduces inside a living cell.

INDEX

K

Korea, 56

L

Labs
  uConnect, 9, 64
  uDemonstrate, 60–63
    Modeling Mutations, 98–99
  uInvestigate, 15, 18, 21, 29, 32, 36, 40, 46, 50, 51, 52, 66, 74, 76, 84, 87
Laundry detergents, 60–63
Leaves, 53
Leopard flounders, *81*
Literacy Connection
  Analyze Text Structure, 53
  Cite Textual Evidence, 35
  Corroborate, 85
  Determine Conclusions, 22
  Determine Meaning, 71
  Integrate with Visuals, 79
  Summarize Text, 42
  see also **Reading and Literacy Skills**

M

Make meaning, 68
Male cones, *35*
Mallard ducks, *67*
Manipulation, **86**
Malnutrition, *56*
Mammals, 44–45
Marmots, *58*
Math Connection
  Construct a Scatter Plot, 77
  Construct Graphs, 69
  Determine Probability, 23
  Distinguish Relationships, 15
  Draw Comparative Inferences, 45
  Model with Mathematics, 69
  Represent Quantitative Relationships, 56
  Summarize Distributions, 15
  Synthesize Information, 56
Math Toolbox
  Determining Probability, 23
  Human Malnutrition and Height, 56

Sexual Reproduction, 15
Survivorship Curves, 45
Mating behaviors, 42–43
Mating systems, **42**
Mendel, Gregor, 19, 67, 91
Mendel's experiments, 19–20, 22, 24
Mice, 16
Migration, **47**
Milky Way, 95
Model It!, 14, 18, 37, 42, 70
Monogamy, 42
mRNA, 78
Mutagens, 80
Mutations
  camouflage and, *81*
  defined, **78**
  DNA and, *78, 79*
  effects of, 81
  environmental factors and, 80–81
  genetic, 78
  harmful, 81
  helpful, 81
  neutral, 81
  in reproduction, 82
  screening for, 91
  sex-linked, 78
  types of, 78–79

N

Negative gravitropism, *52*
North Korea, 56
Northern elephant seals, *74–75*
Nuclei, *68*
Nucleotides, 95
Nutrients
  for animals, 55
  for plants, 54

O

Offspring, 14, 20
Orcas, *46*
Organ systems, **53**
Organisms, 13, 14, 15.
  see also **Animals; Plants**
Ovaries, *36*
Ovules, **35**, *36*

P

P generation, *20*
Palm trees, *51*
Parental investment, 44
Parenting behavior, *45*
Parents, 20
Peas, 20–21, *22, 26,* 67
Pedigrees, 70, 72
Petals, *36*
Phenotypes, **26**
Pheromones, **43**
Photoperiodism, **53**
Phototropism, 52
Plasmids, *87*
Pistils, *36*
Plan It!, 20, 54, 86
Plants
  asexual reproduction, 34
  diseases and, 54
  environmental conditions and, 54
  growth, *53*
  nutrients and, 51
  reproduction of, 32
  responses and growth, 52–54
  seasonal change and, 53
  structures for reproduction, 34–37
  water and, 54
Pods, *46*
Polar bears, 47
Pollen, 35–36
Pollen tubes, *36*
Pollination, **19**, 20
Pollinators, *36*
Polygenetic inheritance, 28
Polygynandry, 42
Polygyny, 42
Positive phototropism, *52*
Privacy laws, *92*
Probability, **23**–25
Process skills, *see* **Science and Engineering Practices (SEP)**
Project Based Learning. *see* **Quest**
Proteins
  changes in, 82
Punnet squares, *24–25,* 76
Purebred, *22,* 26, 27, *85*

INDEX

* Page numbers for charts, graphs, maps, and pictures are printed in italics. Page numbers for definitions are printed in boldface.

CREDITS

Photography

Photo locators denoted as follows: Top (T), Center (C), Bottom (B), Left (L), Right (R), Background (Bkgrd)

Covers

Front: Don Johnston/All Canada Photos/Getty Images; Back: Marinello/DigitalVision Vectors/Getty Images

Instructional Segment 3

iv: Nick Lundgren/Shutterstock; vi: Kelly vanDellen/ Alamy Stock Photo; vii: Dr P. Marazzi/Science Source; viii: Fabriziobalconi/Fotolia; ixBkgrd: Brian J. Skerry/National Geographic/Getty Images; ixB: Dale Kolke/ZUMA Press/ Newscom; 000: Sacramento Bee/ZUMAPRESS/Newscom; 002L: Mark Conlin/Alamy Stock Photo; 002R: Hector Amezcua/ ZUMA Press/Newscom; 003: Wrangel/123RF; 005T: Education Images/UIG/Getty Images; 005BL: Kevin Schafer/Alamy Stock Photo; 005BR: Bill_Dally/iStock/Getty Images Plus/ Getty Images; 006: Sacramento Bee/ZUMAPRESS/Newscom; 008-009: Kelly vanDellen/Alamy Stock Photo; 010-011: Rickyd/Shutterstock; 012-013: Draleksun/Fotolia; 013L: Alan J. S. Weaving/ardea.com/AGE Fotostock; 013R: Biosphoto/ SuperStock; 014T: Bill & Brigitte Clough/Design Pics Inc/Alamy Stock Photo; 014B: cbimages/Alamy Stock Photo; 016: Les Gibbon/Alamy Stock Photo; 019: Jeff Goulden/Getty Images; 022: Martin Shields/Alamy Stock Photo; 023: James Steidl/ Shutterstock; 024: Martin Shields/Alamy Stock Photo; 025: Martin Shields/Alamy Stock Photo; 026: Martin Shields/Alamy Stock Photo; 028: Kadmy/Fotolia; 029: Danita Delimont/Alamy Stock Photo; 030: Kali9/Getty Images; 032-033: Gino Santa Maria/Shutterstock; 034T: Inga Spence/Alamy Stock Photo; 034B: Barsan Attila/Shutterstock; 035L: Krystyna Szulecka/ Alamy Stock Photo; 035R: WILDLIFE GmbH/Alamy Stock Photo; 039T: NASA; 039B: NASA; 040-041: Jaynes Gallery/ Danita Delimont/Alamy Stock Photo; 043: Steve Shinn/ Alamy Stock Photo; 044: Kitch Bain/Shutterstock; 046T: Tony Wu/Nature Picture Library; 046B: Morley Read/Alamy Stock Photo; 050-051: Bill Gorum/Alamy Stock Photo; 052L: Cathy Melloan/Alamy Stock Photo; 052R: Martin Shields/ Alamy Stock Photo; 053L: Artens/Shutterstock; 053C: Patjo/ Shutterstock; 053R: Haru/Shutterstock; 054: Panuwat Kanisarn/ Shutterstock; 055: Alex Staroseltsev/Shutterstock; 058: Nina B/Shutterstock; 066-067: Cuppyuppycake Creative/ Getty Images; 073T: MixAll Studio Creative/Getty Images; 073B: Miodrag Gajic/Getty Images; 074-075: Marc Moritsch/ National Geographic Creative/Alamy Stock Photo; 080L: D. Kucharski & K. Kucharska/Shutterstock; 080R: Dragon Images/ Shutterstock; 081: Aquapix/Shutterstock; 082: Inga Ivanova/ Shutterstock; 084: Eriklam/123RF; 086: Reuters/Alamy Stock Photo; 088T: Eye of Science/Science Source; 088B: Coneyl Jay/ Getty Images; 089: Clive Gee/AP Images; 090: M. Watson/ Ardea/AGE Fotostock; 095: Panther Media GmbH/Alamy Stock Photo.

Take Notes

Use this space for recording notes and sketching out ideas.